THERE ARE ALMOST 7 BILLION REASONS WHY WE SHOULD WORK TOGETHER.

As the world's population approaches seven billion, the challenges facing humanity have never been greater. Fortunately, the solutions to many of the most fundamental challenges can be found in science. But providing for the food, energy and safety needs of a growing population will require more than science alone. It will require many people working together. People who can collaborate across borders, companies, governments, organizations and cultures to devise solutions—both large and small—that improve the lives of people around the world.

DuPont has a rich history of scientific discovery that has enabled countless innovations and made life better for people everywhere. And today, we're working with more people, in more places, to make life the best that it can be. *Welcome to The Global Collaboratory.*

Visit dupont.com/collaboratory to learn more.

GETHER, WE CAN PROTECT WHAT MATTERS MOST.

ur population grows, so do the threats to human safety and well-being. Globally, over 1,000,000 people per lose their lives to workplace injuries alone. DuPont is working with *companies, governments, academics and tists* on a vast range of materials, products and consulting solutions that protect life and our environment.

orking with companies around the world, DuPont s provided workplace safety training to over million people.

3,000

HUMAN LIVES
More than 3,000 law enforcement lives have been saved by wearing body armor, as documented by the IACP/DuPont™ Kevlar Survivors' Club®.

Dark-mantled Sooty Albatross *(Phoebetria fusca)*
Size: Head and body length, 84 - 89 cm; wingspan, approx. 200 cm
Weight: Males approx. 2.7 kg; females approx. 2.4 kg **Habitat:** Ranges throughout South Atlantic and Indian Oceans **Surviving number:** Estimated at 42,000

Photographed by Tui De Roy

WILDLIFE AS CANON SEES IT

Away from it all. When breeding season rolls around, the dark-mantled sooty albatross builds its nests on nearly inaccessible ledges in some of the most rugged and least visited islands of the South Atlantic and Indian Oceans. As a result of this seclusion, its life is largely shrouded in mystery. It is known, however, that the female lays but a single egg, which both parents take turns incubating. If a couple successfully raises a chick one year, they will seldom breed again the following year. With a slow rate of reproduction and a perilously high rate of at-sea mortality, the enigmatic seafarer is in danger of going away forever.

As we see it, we can help make the world a better place. Raising awareness of endangered species is just one of the ways we at Canon are taking action—for the good of the planet we call home. Visit **canon.com/environment** to learn more.

Canon

NATIONAL GEOGRAPHIC

JANUARY 2011 · VOL. 219 · NO. 1

70

On the Cover Emblematic of our populous world, Shanghai has 14 million people, 2.3 million vehicles, and 9,320 miles of roads.
Photo by Peter Bialobrzeski, Laif/Redux

 ngm.com Even a non-spelunker can crawl through the two-and-a-half-mile passageway of Vietnam's giant cave, courtesy of our interactive graphic.

FOR SUBSCRIPTIONS, GIFT MEMBERSHIPS, OR CHANGES OF ADDRESS, CONTACT CUSTOMER SERVICE AT NGMSERVICE.COM, OR CALL 1-800-NGS-LINE (647-5463). OUTSIDE THE U.S. AND CANADA PLEASE CALL +1-813-979-6845.

EDITOR'S NOTE

Crowds surge during the annual Rath Yatra Hindu festival in Puri, India.

The world's population will reach seven billion this year. But you don't need to visit Delhi, India (population 22 million), or China (home to a fifth of the world's people) to grasp the consequences. When I return to Jackson County, Oregon, where I was born, the green fields where I used to cut hay, dig onions, and harvest pears are gone. They have been replaced by subdivisions and big-box stores. This is hardly a surprise given that the population of Jackson County has more than tripled in my lifetime. When I see the rapid development going on in my hometown, I can't help but wonder what the future holds for the rest of the world.

This month we begin exploring that future with a series of stories about population that will run throughout the year. Environment editor Robert Kunzig starts by sketching out a natural history of population. The issues associated with population growth seem endless: poverty, food and water supply, world health, climate change, deforestation, fertility rates, and more.

Kunzig writes, "There may be some comfort in knowing that people have long been alarmed about population." Some of the first papers on demography were written in the 17th century. It's more than 300 years later, and we are still grappling with the outcome of *People* v. *Planet.* We look forward to exploring the topic with you.

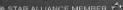

THAI
50th
ANNIVERSARY
1960-2010

Seek the far corners of
Indochina on THAI.

THAI takes you to the enchanting possibilities of the best of Indochina

The mysteries of Vietnam, Cambodia, Laos, and Myanmar are yours to uncover.
Enjoy out legendary service throughout Indochina, or to any of our
destinations across 5 continents, and discover a world that's
smooth as silk. What are you waiting for?

USA

Asia

NATIONAL GEOGRAPHIC

Inspiring people to care about the planet

The National Geographic Society is chartered in Washington, D.C., as a nonprofit scientific and educational organization "for the increase and diffusion of geographic knowledge." Since 1888 the Society has supported more than 9,000 explorations and research projects, adding to knowledge of earth, sea, and sky.

 Please recycle.

LETTERS

September 2010

King Tut's Family Secrets

DNA evidence is revealing truths about King Tut, his family, and ancient Egypt, but I wonder if these fact-finding, theory-crushing, gung-ho missions are taking away some of the mystique of those times.
True, the more we know about history, the more we know about ourselves, and this can only be good. However, in our quest for every detail, I fear we will gradually erode the most appealing quality of all history: the unknown.

DEAN WATSON
Warranwood, Victoria

I read with interest of the search for a possible cause of King Tut's death. As a cardiovascular specialist, I believe a likely cause (which may not leave a trace on the mummy) was omitted from the differential diagnosis. Partial leg disability can lead at any time to formation of blood clots in the veins of the diseased leg. Migration of these clots to the arteries of the lungs can be fatal.

TALI T. BASHOUR
Clinical Professor of Medicine
University of California
San Francisco, California

Madagascar's Pierced Heart

While the United States and the European Union have enacted legislation designed to prevent importation of endangered plant and animal products from Madagascar and elsewhere, this legislation has had little impact in the Third World countries that are home to many of these species. In 2008 the U.S. Congress amended the Lacey Act to require that imports with plant or animal components brought into the U.S. be accompanied by a declaration of all species used in those components and that they were harvested legally in the country of origin. The European Union has similar legislation. China and Japan, members of the World Trade Organization, have not enacted such legislation, so many products that are illegal to import here remain legal to import into those countries.

GEORGE GRUHN
Nashville, Tennessee

The Ambatovy Project, a nickel- and cobalt-mining operation under construction in Madagascar, began its environmental impact assessment in the 1990s and received its environmental permit in 2006. It received its certification under Madagascar's large-mining investment law, put in place by the previous government, in 2007. It is incorrect to imply, as the photo caption on page 97 does, that the project is akin to illegal logging and the result of a deal brokered with the current transitional government. Our pipeline has been carefully routed to bypass areas of environmental significance. We traverse only about one mile of primary forest, while the remainder of the pipeline avoids all forests apart from a few miles of secondary growth, as shown in your photograph. With the aim to cause no net harm to biodiversity, we have earmarked about 58 square miles of primary forest adjacent to construction sites and elsewhere for conservation and compensation.

ANDREW COOKE
Manager, Environment
Ambatovy Project
Antananarivo, Madagascar

The photo caption on page 97 refers to the broad ecological setting of the mining operation, located in one of Madagascar's critically important, biodiverse regions. Our statement about the government's change of priorities in relation to mining is not a comment on Ambatovy's specific project.

As part of an environmental education unit during our Peace Corps service in Madagascar, we showed elementary school children in our rural village five photos of nature in Madagascar with lots of trees and five photos of ugly industrial areas in the capital without a tree in sight. All the children preferred the industrial photos over the nature photos. When we asked them to explain, they said, "There are cars; there are buildings." In other words, the ugly pictures, to them, were images of prosperity.

CHARLES AND JULIA McNALLY
New York, New York

Contact Us

Email ngsforum@ngm.com
Write National Geographic Magazine, PO Box 98199, Washington, DC 20090-8199. Include name, address, and daytime telephone. Letters may be edited for clarity and length.

What makes this city smarter than any other?

In TheSmarterCity, police fight crime with data. Roads and rails talk to commuters. Students can connect with teachers, wherever they are. Patients fill out healthcare forms only once. Information flows over power lines. TheSmarterCity isn't a vision of tomorrow, it's a vision of today, inspired by ideas happening in cities all over the world. Let's build a smarter planet.

Visit **ibm.com**/thesmartercity/uk

The portrayal of rampant logging that is occurring in the forests of Madagascar troubles me as a professional musician. Many of my friends play piccolo, oboe, and clarinet, and all of us have instruments made of either grenadilla or rosewood. It seems the use of these woods became standardized long ago due to the sound quality one can achieve. When I purchased a new piccolo, I was able to choose between some very colorful wood: purple, green, every shade of brown. Until I read this article, I never stopped to think about where this wood comes from, how risky the logging process can be for the desperate workers, and how endangered these trees really are. Buying instruments made from this wood will not likely cease (as, I imagine, neither will production of dining sets in China), but I hope that understanding the overwhelming deforestation of these threatened species will persuade us to become more mindful of the future of these prized woods.

MARIA E. SCHWARTZ
Chicago, Illinois

As a big tree-lover in double meaning (I'm a woman who is six feet, six inches tall), I was touched by the reportage from Madagascar about the environmental difficulties and the poverty the people are fighting. I am curious about rosewood and how it is sold. What is the Chinese government doing to stop the import and sale of rosewood? It was written that most of it goes to China—but I believe that the Chinese are many times merely the traders. Just as with blood diamonds, the more steps in the chain of sellers, the further away from the truth the items come, and the more buyers think that they are buying something legal. The same question could be put to the American government. Just attacking a certain guitar brand won't do. It's a question of mentality, of making the majority of people who are the final buyers understand that this wood should never have been cut.

LOUISE EKLÖF
Brussels, Belgium

Eels: Mystery Travelers

Thank you for a wonderful article about this mysterious fish-snake. You also cleared up a mystery—so, they do slither over land on a rainy night. That explains how they got to that drowned gravel pit where I night fished for them as a kid. That pond was at least three miles from a river connected to the Baltic Sea

> There were numerous legends attached to eels. If you got a big one, you had to be careful he did not wrap around your arm and break it, just like a boa constrictor. We also thought they were vile scavengers.

and involved a steep climb uphill. We just threw a baited hook into the water and tied the end of the line to the nearest bush. Then we checked the lines every hour or so. When the line was taut, there was an eel at the end of it. There were numerous legends attached to eels. If you got a big one, you had to be careful he did not wrap around your arm and break it, just like a boa constrictor. We also thought they were vile scavengers. The favorite story was of drowning victims being pulled from the river with their body cavities full of eels. None of that was enough to stop us from enjoying them on the dinner table: smoked, in soup, and my favorite, in aspic. A special treat was to go to the fish market to witness fishwives using fresh eels as weapons in a dispute. It was great fun to watch, until the police arrived to break up the fight.

HANS-JUERGEN KIRSTEIN
St. Albert, Alberta

I recall my father telling me about the eel weirs in the Oneida River in Caughdenoy, New York, he saw as a child. I believe they were long out of use by then, but still visible. He told me all about the eel trade that went on in bygone days. I think that the lock system on the canal spelled an end to the eel movements in that river system.

NORMA CONEY
Middleburgh, New York

Visions of Earth

The satellite image of the Davis-Monthan Air Force Base boneyard was very interesting, especially when I turned it upside down and squinted. It didn't take too much imagination to conjure the image of a death's-head, or perhaps a pixelated close-up of the figure in Edvard Munch's painting "The Scream."

DAVID KAMM
Decorah, Iowa

Powerful, yet eco-friendly engines, high specification levels and our pioneering 7 year warranty. The new Sportage urban crossover range delivers the style and versatility to give you the confidence to express your adventurous side.

ia.co.uk

The new Sportage. A bit more adventurous.

EDITORS' CHOICE

Daniel Casares Román Jerez de la Frontera, Spain

The 34-year-old Casares spent nearly ten months in South America, part of his ongoing project to photograph indigenous cultures. After trekking to a remote village in the Peruvian Amazon, he documented this Mayoruna woman resting in a hammock after gathering cassava, her face adorned with the traditional piercings and tattoos of her tribe.

Rakesh Chandode Greifswald, Germany

When Chandode, 27, visits a new city or country, his camera is always drawn to statues and monuments. His first trip to Prague was no exception. On the Charles Bridge he came across the "Lamentation of Christ" sculpture—and noticed a spiderweb on the faces of Jesus and Mary. "It made the moment more intense and sad," he says.

Every month this page features two photographs: one chosen by our editors, one chosen by our readers via online voting. For more information, go to *ngm.com/yourshot.*

READERS' CHOICE

far out just got a little closer.

Come knowing what you want to see.

And see what you do not know.

Lose track of days. Discover endless tranquility.

Take it all in. Through your eyes, your ears, your hands, your soul.

And leave with a new found sense of discovery.

Abu Dhabi. Travellers welcome.

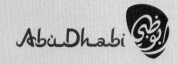

China Towering ice sculptures set a winter night ablaze with color at the 26th annual Harbin International Ice and Snow Festival. The monuments, showcasing architecture from palaces to pagodas, stood for more than a month.

Germany A diver polishing glass joins a radiant display of sea life in a giant saltwater tank at Berlin's Radisson Blu Hotel. The ring-shaped AquaDom, some 80 feet high with an elevator inside, holds about 1,500 tropical fish.

PHOTO: SEAN GALLUP, GETTY IMAGES

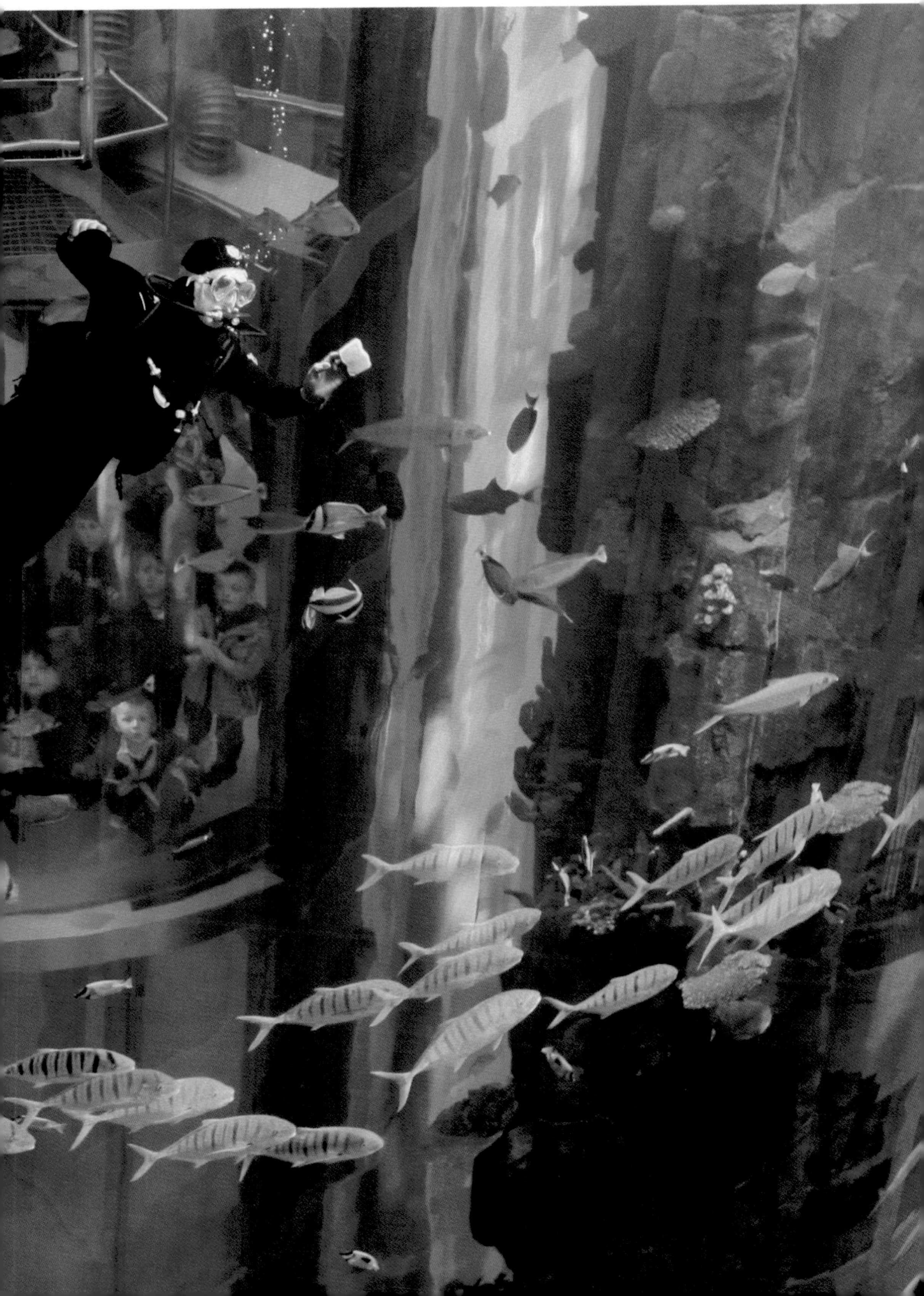

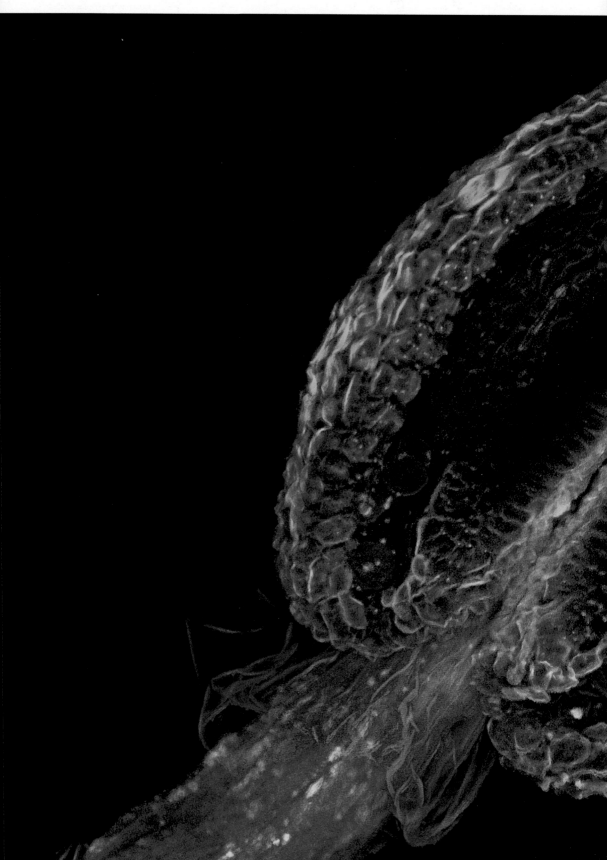

Estonia Bursting with luminosity under fluorescent dyes and laser beams, a pollen-producing structure from a thale cress glows under a microscope. The plant's small genome makes it a favorite subject for genetic research.

PHOTO: HEITI PAVES

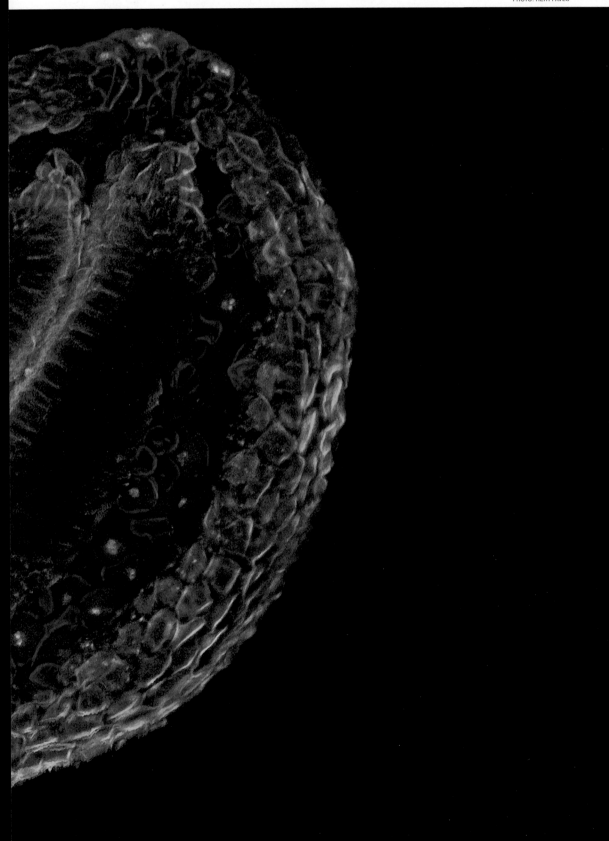

P O P U L A T I O N

7 SEVEN BILLION

World Party As the global population approaches the seven billion mark, we should all probably try to get to know one another a little better. What if somebody threw a party and invited every single person living on Earth? It would be a logistical nightmare, but you might be surprised at the relatively small size of the venue needed to fit seven billion people—even if we gave them enough room to dance. Don't forget to RSVP. —*Nigel Holmes*

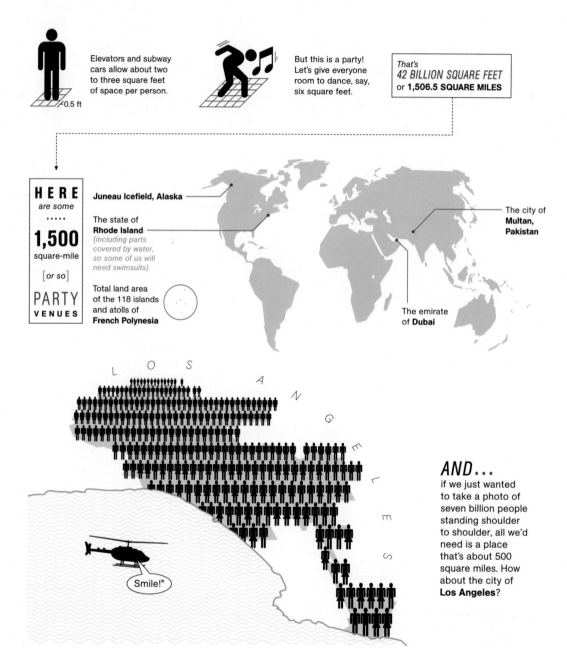

Elevators and subway cars allow about two to three square feet of space per person.

0.5 ft

But this is a party! Let's give everyone room to dance, say, six square feet.

That's
42 BILLION SQUARE FEET
or **1,506.5 SQUARE MILES**

HERE *are some* • • • • • **1,500** square-mile [*or so*] **PARTY VENUES**

Juneau Icefield, Alaska

The state of **Rhode Island** *(including parts covered by water, so some of us will need swimsuits)*

Total land area of the 118 islands and atolls of **French Polynesia**

The city of **Multan, Pakistan**

The emirate of **Dubai**

LOS ANGELES

Smile!*

AND...
if we just wanted to take a photo of seven billion people standing shoulder to shoulder, all we'd need is a place that's about 500 square miles. How about the city of **Los Angeles**?

✱ If the photographer said "smile" in the 6,900-some languages spoken in the world today, we'd be standing there for about an hour.

GRAPHIC: NIGEL HOLMES

"Don't drink the water."

Armchair travel journalist

44°N – Junction City, USA

Are you living a life without boundaries?

Some well-meant advice is best ignored, but it's still good to know you're covered when you're away. With HSBC Premier, your family is protected with both Travel Insurance and dedicated assistance when you're abroad. Which is reassuring to know when you're making the most of life.

www.hsbcpremier.com

HSBCPremier

HSBC

The world's local bank

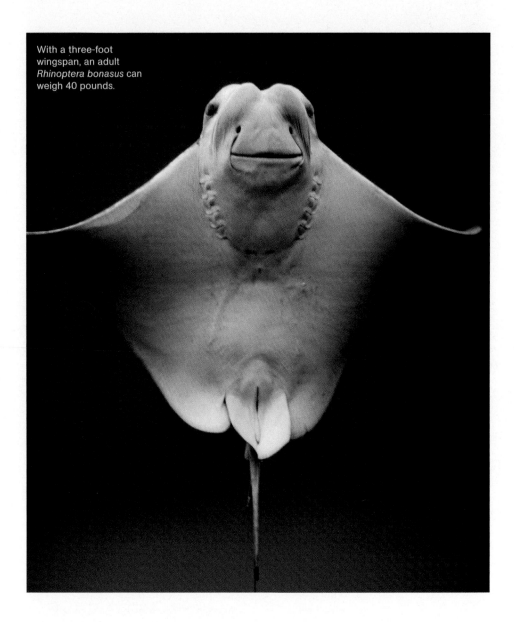

With a three-foot wingspan, an adult *Rhinoptera bonasus* can weigh 40 pounds.

Eat a Ray, Save the Bay?
Cownose rays swarm the Chesapeake Bay each summer, taxing an already fragile ecosystem by gobbling shellfish and roiling grass beds. Shaped like kites, they taste like tuna—a meaty mouthfeel packed with lean protein. Now area officials see a potential win-win: Whet human appetites with a tasteful name ("Chesapeake ray") and rebalance the bay.

Rays aren't invasive newcomers here; in 1608 one stung explorer John Smith. But as predators like coastal sharks have declined, the observed spike in cownoses, though untallied, could be grounds for a carefully monitored fishery—and new revenue streams for watermen, retailers, and localities. Call it the new calamari? *—Jeremy Berlin*

PHOTO: HENRY HORENSTEIN, GETTY IMAGES. NGM MAPS

More possibilities on the go.

7" Tablet
Samsung GALAXY Tab

CULTURE

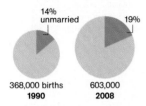

Births to U.S. women 35 and older

14% unmarried

19%

368,000 births
1990

603,000
2008

Modern Mothering

More U.S. women are having children later in life, according to a new study from the Pew Research Center. Some possible reasons: higher education, fertility treatments, and changing attitudes toward marriage. While the overall birthrate in 2008 didn't vary much from 1990, the number of babies born to women 35 and older rose a staggering 64 percent.

Another factor, notes report co-author Gretchen Livingston, is that younger people were more likely than older ones to cite the economic downturn as a reason to delay pregnancy. Women in their late 30s to 40s "don't really have that choice."

The same Pew report found that a record 41 percent of 2008 births occurred outside of marriage, up from 28 percent in 1990. And though most were to women under 25, older mothers are also less likely to be married these days. Which is not to say these moms are going it alone. The trend "comes largely from births to women who are co-habiting with the child's father," says sociologist R. Kelly Raley. "It's clear that we think differently today than we did several decades ago." —*Cara Birnbaum*

Today's mothers include more women who are older and, increasingly, unmarried.

PHOTO: REBECCA HALE, NGM STAFF
GRAPHIC: MINA LIU. SOURCE: PEW RESEARCH CENTER

More to applaud on the go.

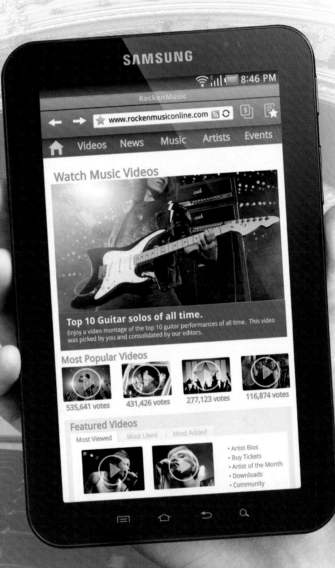

7" Tablet
Samsung GALAXY Tab

| Web Browsing with Flash | eReader | Google Maps™ Navigation (Beta) | Augmented Reality | Video Conferencing | Multimedia |

Coloring by Structure

For years scientists have known that pigments aren't the only way butterflies get their brilliant colors. Light can also bounce off structures and reflect hues through scattering or interference, as with the blue of the sky or the iridescence of a soap bubble. Now a group at Yale University has identified one such structure in five butterfly species as a gyroid—a complex, three-dimensional form that is one of nature's most efficient ways of folding space (left).

Parides sesostris

In the butterflies studied, from the Papilionidae and Lycaenidae families, the microscopic gyroids consist of chitin—the same material found in insect exoskeletons—and air pockets interwoven in a repeating pattern that resembles a network of three-bladed boomerangs. The green color resulting from the interplay of scattered light helps warn off predators, says lead scientist Richard Prum. Gyroids have superior optical properties, and the ability to synthesize similar forms could aid in the development of solar cells and insulation for fiber-optic cables.

While the majority of butterfly colors are pigmentary—created when molecules absorb and reemit certain wavelengths of light— a variety of structural ones exist. So far green is the only known gyroid color, says Prum, "but I'm sure there are more." —*Luna Shyr*

Scales on wing surface

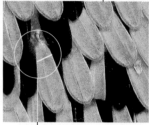

Cross section of a scale

Gyroids

Gyroids, seen here in a colorized electron microscope scan, produce this butterfly's green hues.

PHOTOS: MARTIN OEGGERLI, WITH MARCO CANTONI, ÉCOLE POLYTECHNIQUE FÉDÉRALE DE LAUSANNE (ABOVE);
MARTIN OEGGERLI (MIDDLE); RICHARD PRUM, YALE UNIVERSITY (TOP). ART: SHIZUKA AOKI

More delight on the go.

SAMSUNG

t I: The Old Buccaneer

ea-dog at the Admiral Benbow

TRELAWNEY, Dr. Livesey, and the
se gentlemen having asked me to
m the whole particulars about Trea-
d, from the beginning to the end,
othing back but the bearings of the
island, and that only because there is still trea-
sure not yet lifted, I take up my pen in the year
of grace 17_ and go back to the time when my
father kept the Admiral Benbow inn and the
brown old seaman with the sabre cut first took
up his lodging under our roof.

I remember him as if it were yesterday, as he
came plodding to the inn door, his sea-chest
following behind him in a hand-barrow--a tall,
strong, heavy, nut-brown man, his tarry pigtail
falling over the shoulder of his soiled blue
coat, his hands ragged and scarred, with black,

PART I: THE OLD BUCCANEER — 1 of 11

7" Tablet
Samsung GALAXY Tab

Web Browsing   eReader   Google Maps™   Augmented   Video   Multimedia
with Flash   Navigation (Beta)   Reality   Conferencing

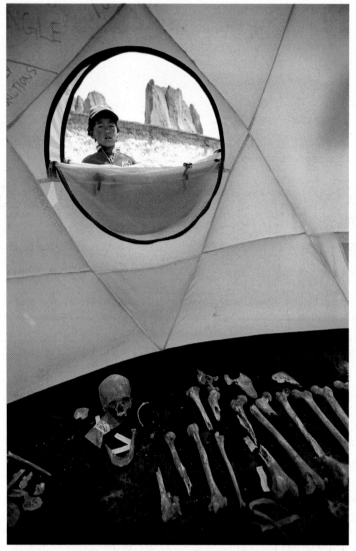

A Nepalese child peers into a tent sheltering remains as old as 2,500 years.

NG GRANTEE

Cliff Cave Secrets

Archaeologist Mark Aldenderfer set out last year to explore remote cliffside caves in Nepal's Mustang district, aiming to find human remains near an ancient settlement high in the Himalaya. Almost at once, he came face-to-face with what he was seeking: Jutting out from the rock, he recalls, 13,000 feet up, "a skull was looking at me right as I was looking at it."

The skull, dating back perhaps 2,500 years, was among many human bones piled inside several burial caves. Aldenderfer and his team hope that DNA analysis will help pinpoint the origins of this isolated region's inhabitants, who may have migrated from the Tibetan Plateau or points south.

Nearby, Aldenderfer's colleagues in 2008 also found 8,000 manuscripts at least 500 years old, similar to one (below) found in 2010. Their contents are still being deciphered, but scholars say they will shed new light on Bon, the indigenous religion that predated Buddhism in ancient Tibet and still exists in a few pockets. "These caves," says Aldenderfer, "offer marvelous insights." —Hannah Bloch

ENVIRONMENT

Belgian Heat Survey A nighttime flight over Antwerp, Belgium, last winter sought to separate the naughty from the nice. But it wasn't slumbering children who were being judged; it was the buildings that housed them. That's because in 2009 Antwerp and 20 other Flemish municipalities hired the geo-information firm Eurosense to create an aerial thermographic image showing how much heat was escaping through city roofs. A poorly insulated one can account for about 30 percent of a building's total energy loss.

In this image (below right), the least efficient buildings and the city streets glow a bright red. Newer, more sustainable buildings—often insulated with materials such as spray foam or rock wool—appear as a cooler blue or green. Getting the full picture, however, requires a visit to the website *zoominopuwdak.antwerpen.be*, which lets residents plug in their addresses to learn how their building fares, as well as which government-sponsored loans and grants are available to those who improve their home's energy efficiency.

Now other cities in Belgium, as well as five in France and one in Germany, are following Antwerp's lead—a sign that in some parts of Europe, coal deliveries will be down in December. —*Aaron Britt*

Daytime aerial photograph of Antwerp

Nighttime aerial thermogram of Antwerp

Streets and badly insulated buildings give off heat at night and appear red; foliage and well-insulated structures look blue or green. Thermal colors also depend on roof shape (flat or slanted), roofing materials, and thermostat settings.

SOURCES: CITY OF ANTWERP; EUROSENSE; FLEMISH GEOGRAPHICAL INFORMATION AGENCY. NGM MAPS

The greatest true story never told… until now.

The Way Back, which premieres in U.K. cinemas on December 26, is an epic story of survival, solidarity, and indomitable human will. It's a compelling human journey directed by six-time Academy Award nominee Peter Weir and co-produced by National Geographic Entertainment.

The story is inspired by the acclaimed book *The Long Walk: The True Story of a Trek to Freedom,* as well as first-person accounts and anecdotes from survivors and their families. Indeed, Weir's fastidious research and painstaking pursuit of realism reflects the film's close association with National Geographic. In fact, back issues of *National Geographic* magazine proved an invaluable resource for costume and set designs.

The film follows seven prisoners who escape from the horrors of a gulag during Stalin's Great Terror. The group escape into the frozen forests of Siberia, where temperatures can drop below minus 70°F. Utterly unprepared and with a faltering sense of direction, they set off on a 4,500-mile trek to the safety of British India—a journey that defies any reasonable chance of success.

Director Peter Weir *(Master and Commander)* has assembled an impressive cast—Jim Sturgess, Ed Harris, Saoirse Ronan, and Colin Farrell.

The film recounts the relentless challenges the survivors faced during their journey. The overcrowded and claustrophobic confines of the gulag, meticulously recreated in every harrowing detail, contrast starkly with the vast Mongolian plains—a landscape so breathtakingly remote you can see the curvature of the Earth without spying a single sign of man. The scorching torments of the Gobi desert give way to the impracticable heights of the Himalaya, as one impossibly hostile terrain leads to the next.

No stone was left unturned in the telling of this remarkable true story, because real life is often more remarkable than fiction.

The Way Back opens in U.K. cinemas December 26.

NATIONAL GEOGRAPHIC
ENTERTAINMENT

This spiny turtle, like other turtles, has an upper shell that forms as ribs widen and fuse into a bony plate.

Cracking the Shell
Never mind Aesop and his fables. Japanese scientists are telling a new story of how the turtle got its shell.

A shield from the elements and from predators, as well as a mineral reserve in low-oxygen environments, the turtle's shell is unique in vertebrate anatomy. Still, a turtle's embryo starts out looking like any spined animal's—say, a chicken's or a mouse's. But about a third of the way through in-ovo development, says Shigeru Kuratani of the Riken Center for Developmental Biology, "an anatomical rule is violated" that remaps the animal's physique. The ribs grow over the shoulder blades instead of under them as humans' do, forcing the body wall to fold in on itself. What would have been an internal rib cage fuses into a bony plate under the skin and becomes a part of the turtle's outer armor.

In 2008 the fossil record delivered elegant support for this theory—and for another, more disputed one: that shells evolved from the bottom up. With a belly plate but an incomplete upper shell, 220-million-year-old *Odontochelys semitestacea*, found in China, seems an in-between form—one that looks a lot like an early stage in modern turtle development. More bony finds may someday tell the rest of the turtle's story. —*Jennifer S. Holland*

SHELL GAME Scientists don't yet know what triggers a turtle's odd anatomy, but they have mapped its progress in the egg.

Early Embryo
A turtle's basic body plan, at first like that of other vertebrates, is already starting to diverge into something unique.

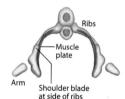

Development
As incubation progresses, the ribs veer outward. The muscle plate then folds as the ribs push over the shoulder blades.

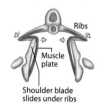

Hatchling The final shell is made of the fused ribs, still fixed to the shoulder blades. In many species, a hard protein layer tops it all off.

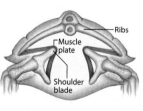

PHOTO: JOEL SARTORE. ART: HIRAM HENRIQUEZ
SOURCE: HIROSHI NAGASHIMA, RIKEN CENTER FOR DEVELOPMENTAL BIOLOGY

Spotting Nature

The Open University

An innovative website is answering questions for nature enthusiasts throughout the U.K. iSpot (***www.ispot.org.uk***) lets anyone from casual observers to experienced wildlife-watchers post photos from cameras or mobiles and have their discoveries identified by an expert or member of the iSpot community. Or, if the person posting knows the name, the site is an ideal place to share the discovery, its location, and see where else it's been sighted. iSpot is part of The Open University's (OU) contribution to the Open Air Laboratories project funded by the Big Lottery Fund for England and has recently been awarded a prize by Wildscreen for its quality and innovation. An OU course, Neighbourhood Nature, complements the site, allowing anyone interested in nature to learn more about how to find, study, and record plants and animals in their area. Thousands of postings of all things furry, flying, and flowering are pouring in from forest paths,

country lanes, and city walkways across the U.K. Website integrity and accuracy have been ensured through the involvement of a wide range of nature experts. The OU's effort to create a site that helps everyone learn and be inspired right where they live, seems to be spot on.

ALL PHOTOS NHPA

With 600 courses from beginner to postgraduate and 250 qualifications, the OU offers a world of learning to 250,000 students each year through podcasts, interactive multi-media materials and online forums. Exceptional quality and choice have helped to place OU in the top three U.K. universities for student satisfaction. The OU and National Geographic Channel are working to raise interest in learning more about our world, and readers can find out more at *www.openuniversity. co.uk/inspiration*.

ABOVE LEFT
BROWN-LIPPED BANDED SNAIL
Cepaea nemoralis
INVERTEBRATES Sussex, U.K.

ABOVE RIGHT
CLUSTERED BONNET
FUNGI *Mycena inclinata*
& LICHENS Cornwall, U.K.

BELOW
COMMA BUTTERFLY
Polygonia c-album resting on *Hibiscus syriacus*
INVERTEBRATES Bournemouth, U.K.

What's left of the Aral Sea lies in present-day Kazakhstan (top third of photo) and Uzbekistan.

Aral Sea Change Seen from a satellite, today's Aral Sea is but a cluster of green globs. The brown, beige, and white? Some 3,240 square miles of dirt, dust, and salt—a toxic mess blown by sandstorms and tied to local health problems and climate changes. In 1960 this was an inland sea the size of Ireland. But heedless river diversion—for irrigation to wrest cotton and rice from the Central Asian desert—and evaporation have shriveled it by 90 percent.

Since 2005 a World Bank–funded dam has revived the northern-most lake's fish and fishing industry. To help restore the rest, says Philip Micklin, geography professor emeritus at Western Michigan University, engineering money and political accord are key. If they don't exist by 2020, much of this water won't either. —*Jeremy Berlin*

Few countries pack as many hidden gems into such a small space as Israel. From the magical mystery of Jerusalem to the rich cultural experiences of the Dead Sea, the energy and excitement of Tel Aviv to the sun and relaxation of Eilat. Israel is the ideal year-round destination.

Unique Experiences
THINKISRAEL.COM/GEMS

Drifting in Static

A rising tide of man-made noise is disrupting the lives of marine animals.

THE DEEP IS DARK, BUT NOT SILENT; it's alive with sounds. Whales and other marine mammals, fish, and even some invertebrates depend on sound, which travels much farther in water than light does. The animals use sound to find food and mates, to avoid predators, and to communicate.

They face a growing problem: Man-made noise is drowning them out. "For many of these animals it's as if they live in cities," says marine scientist Brandon Southall, former director of the National Oceanic and Atmospheric Administration's (NOAA) ocean acoustics program.

Two years ago the problem made it to the U.S. Supreme Court, in a case that might have been called *U.S. Navy* v. *Whales*. The Court's *(Continued)*

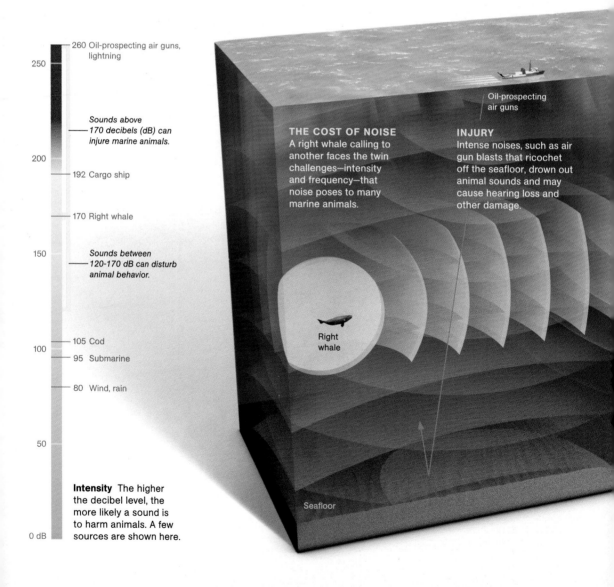

260 Oil-prospecting air guns, lightning

250

Sounds above 170 decibels (dB) can injure marine animals.

200

192 Cargo ship

170 Right whale

150

Sounds between 120-170 dB can disturb animal behavior.

105 Cod

100

95 Submarine

80 Wind, rain

50

Intensity The higher the decibel level, the more likely a sound is to harm animals. A few sources are shown here.

0 dB

THE COST OF NOISE
A right whale calling to another faces the twin challenges—intensity and frequency—that noise poses to many marine animals.

INJURY
Intense noises, such as air gun blasts that ricochet off the seafloor, drown out animal sounds and may cause hearing loss and other damage.

Oil-prospecting air guns

Right whale

Seafloor

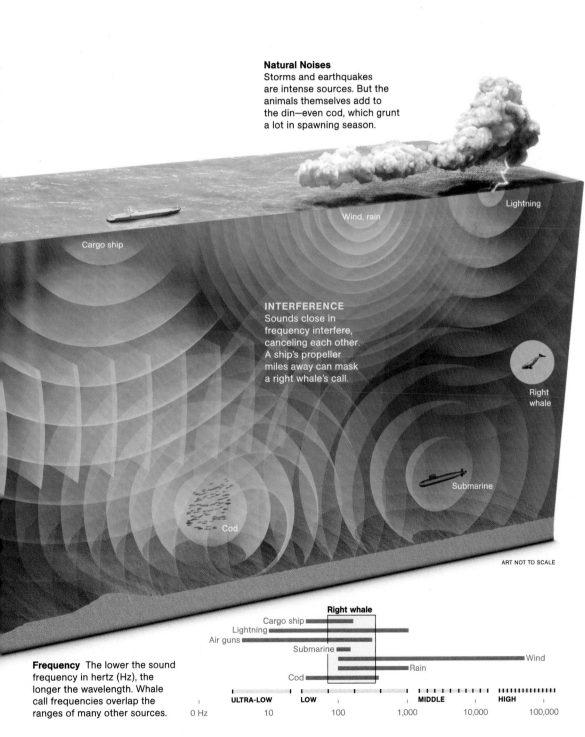

Natural Noises
Storms and earthquakes are intense sources. But the animals themselves add to the din—even cod, which grunt a lot in spawning season.

Lightning

Wind, rain

Cargo ship

INTERFERENCE
Sounds close in frequency interfere, canceling each other. A ship's propeller miles away can mask a right whale's call.

Right whale

Submarine

Cod

ART NOT TO SCALE

Frequency The lower the sound frequency in hertz (Hz), the longer the wavelength. Whale call frequencies overlap the ranges of many other sources.

Right whale

Cargo ship
Lightning
Air guns
Submarine
Wind
Rain
Cod

ULTRA-LOW	LOW		MIDDLE	HIGH	
0 Hz	10	100	1,000	10,000	100,000

GRAPHIC: STEFAN FICHTEL. SOURCES: C. W. CLARK, CORNELL LAB OF ORNITHOLOGY; BRANDON SOUTHALL, UNIVERSITY OF CALIFORNIA, SANTA CRUZ; KATHLEEN VIGNESS-RAPOSA, MARINE ACOUSTICS, INC.

John McCallister included National Geographic in his estate plans.

NATIONAL GEOGRAPHIC

Office of Estate Planning
1145 17th Street NW
Washington, DC 20036

(800) 226 - 4438
plannedgiftinfo@ngs.org
www.nationalgeographic.org/donate

TO MAKE YOUR BEQUEST
to National Geographic, please
use the following language:

"To the National Geographic
Society in Washington, D.C.,
I give _____% of my residuary
estate." Or you can name a fixed
dollar amount.

Inspire Future Generations

An avid traveler and horticulturist, John McCallister was introduced to National Geographic when his aunt sent him a gift subscription to the magazine in the 1940s. "I like everything about National Geographic, what it stands for, and what it accomplishes," John says.

Now retired, John spends his time taking continuing education classes, landscaping his garden, and frequenting art museums, theatre performances, and concerts. John made a bequest gift as a way to support the things he holds dear. "I included National Geographic in my will because I want the Society to be around for future generations," he says.

For more information about how to include us in your estate plans, or to let us know that you have already done so, please contact the Office of Estate Planning.

○ Yes! Please send me information on how to include National Geographic in my will

○ I have already included National Geographic in my will

○ Please send me information on a National Geographic charitable gift annuity

Birthdate(s) _____
Minimum age 45. Payments begin at age 65

Name _____
Address _____
_____
Phone _____
Email _____

Card to cut off and mail in

Mail to: National Geographic Office of Estate Planning
1145 17th Street NW, Washington, DC 20036

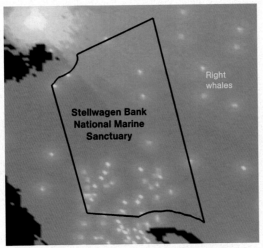

Right whales (pale dots) call to one another in Massachusetts Bay, off Cape Cod. It's a quiet day in April.

A few hours later several ships traverse the area and "bleach" the whales' communication.

decision protected the right of naval vessels to test submarine-hunting sonar systems, whose intense sound pulses have been linked to several mass whale strandings. But the Navy is not the lone villain. Oil company ships towing arrays of air guns fire round-the-clock fusillades loud enough to locate oil buried under the seafloor—and also to be heard hundreds of miles away. Undersea construction operations drive piles into the seafloor and blast holes in it with explosives.

And most of the rising tide of noise—a hundredfold increase since 1960, in many areas—is created simply by the dramatic growth in shipping traffic. "Shipping noise is always there," Southall says. "It doesn't have to be lethal to be problematic over time." The problem is getting steadily worse for another reason. As we're making more noise, we're also making the ocean better at transmitting it. Seawater is absorbing less sound as carbon dioxide from fossil-fuel burning seeps into the ocean and acidifies it.

Noise drives many species of whales, dolphins, and other marine animals to change their behavior markedly—their calling, foraging, and migration patterns—even when it's not enough to drive them onto a beach. Cod and haddock in the Barents Sea have been found to flee the area when air guns start firing, drastically reducing fish catches for days. Large baleen whales are of special concern. They communicate over vast distances in the same frequencies,

around the lowest C on a piano, that ship propellers and engines generate. On most days, says Christopher W. Clark, director of the bioacoustics research program at Cornell University, the area over which whales in coastal waters can hear one another shrinks to only 10 to 20 percent of its natural extent.

Clark studies endangered northern right whales, whose habitat includes busy shipping lanes for the port of Boston. In 2007 he and his colleagues deployed a network of seafloor recorders and automated listening buoys in Massachusetts Bay. From three years of continuous recordings, they then compiled a complete underwater "noise budget." Color animations of the data show the calls of right whales getting all but obliterated as ships pass (see above). "The whales' social network is constantly being ripped and reformed," Clark says. Unable to communicate, individual whales have trouble finding each other and spend more time on their own.

The ten listening buoys now bobbing in Massachusetts Bay could actually help the animals. The researchers are sharing their real-time data on whale locations, transmitted from the buoys via satellite, with tanker captains, who can then slow down their ships or alter course to avoid whales. It's a small note of hope in the din. "Science can only help in so many ways," Clark says. "Then we have to decide whether the animals are important to us." —Leslie Allen

IMAGES: C. W. CLARK, CORNELL LAB OF ORNITHOLOGY; W. ELLISON, MARINE ACOUSTICS, INC.;
L. T. HATCH AND D. WILEY, NOAA SBNMS; S. M. VAN PARIJS, NOAA NEFSC

PULSING WITH PEOPLE

INDIA Its steaming streets crammed with vendors, pedestrians, and iconic Ambassador taxis, Kolkata throbs with some 16 million people—and more pour in every day from small towns. In 1975 only three cities worldwide topped ten million. Today 21 such megacities exist, most in developing countries, where urban areas absorb much of the globe's rising population.

RANDY OLSON

There will soon be **seven billion** people on the planet.

ENERGIZED LANDSCAPE

ENGLAND Glowing furnace bright at night, London became the world's largest city during the coal-powered industrial revolution, a tipping point for the steep rise of Earth's population. Wealthy countries use many times more resources per capita than poorer nations, but as global incomes rise, increased consumption may stress the planet more than population growth.

JASON HAWKES

AGENTS OF CHANGE

SPAIN Immigrants like these Indians at a Sikh festival in Barcelona are bolstering Europe's stagnant population growth rate. Around the world, the childbearing decisions of young women will determine whether global population stabilizes or not. Research shows that the more education a woman receives, the fewer children she is likely to have.

RANDY OLSON

By 2045 global population is projected to reach nine billion. Can the planet take the strain?

As we reach the milestone of seven billion people this year, it's time to take stock. In the coming decades, despite falling birthrates, the population will continue to grow—mostly in poor countries. If the billions of people who want to boost themselves out of poverty follow the path blazed by those in wealthy countries, they too will step hard on the planet's resources. How big will the population actually grow? What will the planet look like in 2045? Throughout the year we'll offer an in-depth series exploring those questions. The answers will depend on the decisions each of us makes.

SOURCES: POPULATION REFERENCE BUREAU AND UNITED NATIONS
PHOTO: FRITZ HOFFMANN

World population
200 MILLION
A.D. 1

9
BILLION
2045

8
BILLION
2024

7
BILLION
2011

6
BILLION
1999

5
BILLION
1987

4
BILLION
1974

3
BILLION
1960

2
BILLION
1930

1
BILLION
1800

RESOURCES THAT CAN BE REPLENISHED, LIKE CHINA'S BAMBOO, WILL BE CRUCIAL.

Projected

BY ROBERT KUNZIG

One day in Delft in the fall of 1677, Antoni van Leeuwenhoek, a cloth merchant who is said to have been the long-haired model for two paintings by Johannes Vermeer—"The Astronomer" and "The Geographer"—abruptly stopped what he was doing with his wife and rushed to his worktable. Cloth was Leeuwenhoek's business but microscopy his passion. He'd had five children already by his first wife (though four had died in infancy), and fatherhood

was not on his mind. "Before six beats of the pulse had intervened," as he later wrote to the Royal Society of London, Leeuwenhoek was examining his perishable sample through a tiny magnifying glass. Its lens, no bigger than a small raindrop, magnified objects hundreds of times. Leeuwenhoek had made it himself; nobody else had one so powerful. The learned men in London were still trying to verify Leeuwenhoek's earlier claims that unseen "animalcules" lived by the millions in a single drop of lake water and even in French wine. Now he had something more delicate to report: Human semen contained animalcules too. "Sometimes more than a thousand," he wrote, "in an amount of material the size of a grain of sand." Pressing the glass to his eye like a jeweler, Leeuwenhoek watched his own animalcules swim about, lashing their long tails. One imagines sunlight falling through leaded windows on a face lost in contemplation, as in the Vermeers. One feels for his wife.

Leeuwenhoek became a bit obsessed after that. Though his tiny peephole gave him privileged access to a never-before-seen microscopic universe, he spent an enormous amount of time looking at spermatozoa, as they're now called. Oddly enough, it was the milt he squeezed from a cod one day that inspired him to estimate, almost casually, just how many people might live on Earth.

Nobody then really had any idea; there were few censuses. Leeuwenhoek started with an estimate that around a million people lived in Holland. Using maps and a little spherical geometry, he calculated that the inhabited land area of the planet was 13,385 times as large as Holland. It was hard to imagine the whole planet being as densely peopled as Holland, which seemed crowded even then. Thus, Leeuwenhoek concluded triumphantly, there couldn't be more than 13.385 billion people on Earth—a small number indeed compared with the 150 billion sperm cells of a single codfish! This cheerful little calculation, writes population biologist Joel Cohen in his book *How Many People Can the Earth Support?*, may have been the first attempt to give a quantitative answer to a question that has become far more pressing now than it was in the 17th century. Most answers these days are far from cheerful.

Historians now estimate that in Leeuwenhoek's day there were only half a billion or so humans on Earth. After rising very slowly for millennia, the number was just starting to take off. A century and a half later, when another scientist reported the discovery of human egg cells, the world's population had doubled to more than a billion. A century after that, around 1930, it had doubled again to two billion. The acceleration since then has been astounding. Before the 20th century, no human had lived through a doubling of the human population, but there are people alive today who have seen it triple. Sometime in late 2011, according to the UN Population Division, there will be seven billion of us.

And the explosion, though it is slowing, is far from over. Not only are people living longer, but so many women across the world are now in their childbearing years—1.8 billion—that the global population will keep growing for another few decades at least, even though each woman is having fewer children than she would have had a generation ago. By 2050 the total number could reach 10.5 billion, or it could stop at eight billion—the difference is about one child per woman. UN demographers consider the middle road their best estimate: They now project that the population may reach nine billion before 2050—in 2045. The eventual tally will depend on the choices individual couples make when they engage in that most intimate of human acts, the one Leeuwenhoek interrupted so carelessly for the sake of science.

With the population still growing by about 80 million each year, it's hard not to be alarmed. Right now on Earth, water tables are falling, soil is eroding, glaciers are melting, and fish stocks are vanishing. Close to a billion people go hungry each day. Decades from now, there will likely be two billion more mouths to feed, mostly in poor countries. There will be billions more people wanting and deserving to boost themselves out of poverty. If they follow the path blazed by wealthy countries—clearing forests, burning coal and oil, freely scattering fertilizers and pesticides—they too will be stepping hard on the planet's natural resources. How exactly is this going to work?

THERE MAY BE SOME COMFORT in knowing that people have long been alarmed about population. From the beginning, says French demographer Hervé Le Bras, demography has been steeped in talk of the apocalypse. Some of the field's founding papers were written just a few years after Leeuwenhoek's discovery by Sir William Petty, a founder of the Royal Society. He estimated that world population would double six times by the Last Judgment, which was expected in about 2,000 years. At that point it would exceed 20 billion people—more, Petty thought, than the planet could feed. "And then, according to the prediction of the Scriptures, there must be wars, and great slaughter, &c.," he wrote.

As religious forecasts of the world's end receded, Le Bras argues, population growth itself provided an ersatz mechanism of apocalypse. "It crystallized the ancient fear, and perhaps the ancient hope, of the end of days," he writes. In 1798 Thomas Malthus, an English priest and economist, enunciated his general law of population: that it necessarily grows faster than the food supply, until war, disease, and famine arrive to reduce the number of people. As it turned out, the last plagues great enough to put a dent in global population had already happened when Malthus wrote. World population hasn't fallen, historians think, since the Black Death of the 14th century.

In the two centuries after Malthus declared that population couldn't continue to soar, that's exactly what it did. The process started in what we now call the developed countries, which were then still developing. The spread of New World crops like corn and the potato, along with the discovery of chemical fertilizers, helped banish starvation in Europe. Growing cities remained cesspools of disease at first, but from the

How Population Booms

As living conditions improve, a country enters successive phases of a process called the demographic transition. The death rate falls, but there's a lag before the birthrate falls too. The result: Population soars. Each phase is marked by a redistribution of the population's age groups, as shown in the pyramids at bottom.

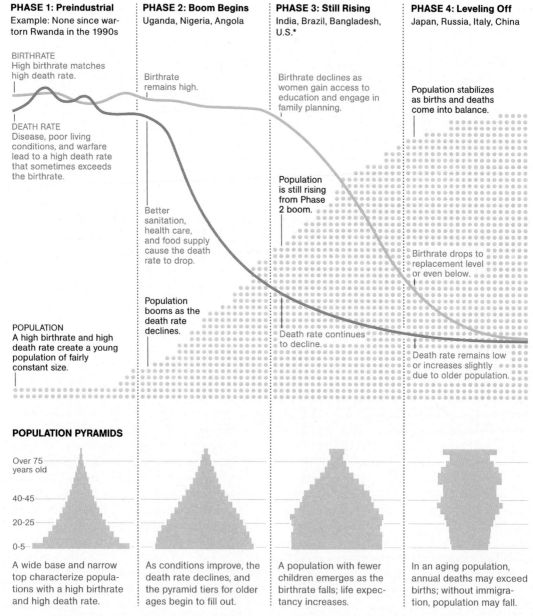

PHASE 1: Preindustrial
Example: None since war-torn Rwanda in the 1990s

BIRTHRATE
High birthrate matches high death rate.

DEATH RATE
Disease, poor living conditions, and warfare lead to a high death rate that sometimes exceeds the birthrate.

POPULATION
A high birthrate and high death rate create a young population of fairly constant size.

PHASE 2: Boom Begins
Uganda, Nigeria, Angola

Birthrate remains high.

Better sanitation, health care, and food supply cause the death rate to drop.

Population booms as the death rate declines.

PHASE 3: Still Rising
India, Brazil, Bangladesh, U.S.*

Birthrate declines as women gain access to education and engage in family planning.

Population is still rising from Phase 2 boom.

Death rate continues to decline.

PHASE 4: Leveling Off
Japan, Russia, Italy, China

Population stabilizes as births and deaths come into balance.

Birthrate drops to replacement level or even below.

Death rate remains low or increases slightly due to older population.

POPULATION PYRAMIDS

Over 75 years old

40-45

20-25

0-5

A wide base and narrow top characterize populations with a high birthrate and high death rate.

As conditions improve, the death rate declines, and the pyramid tiers for older ages begin to fill out.

A population with fewer children emerges as the birthrate falls; life expectancy increases.

In an aging population, annual deaths may exceed births; without immigration, population may fall.

*THE U.S. HAS CHARACTERISTICS OF PHASES 3 AND 4: A RELATIVELY HIGH BIRTHRATE AS WELL AS AN AGING POPULATION.
MARIEL FURLONG, NGM STAFF
SOURCE: CARL HAUB, POPULATION REFERENCE BUREAU

mid-19th century on, sewers began to channel human waste away from drinking water, which was then filtered and chlorinated; that dramatically reduced the spread of cholera and typhus.

Moreover in 1798, the same year that Malthus published his dyspeptic tract, his compatriot Edward Jenner described a vaccine for smallpox—the first and most important in a series of vaccines and antibiotics that, along with better nutrition and sanitation, would double life expectancy in the industrializing countries, from 35 years to 77 today. It would take a cranky person to see that trend as gloomy: "The development of medical science was the straw that broke the camel's back," wrote Stanford population biologist Paul Ehrlich in 1968.

Ehrlich's book, *The Population Bomb*, made him the most famous of modern Malthusians. In the 1970s, Ehrlich predicted, "hundreds of millions of people are going to starve to death," and it was too late to do anything about it. "The cancer of population growth...must be cut out," Ehrlich wrote, "by compulsion if voluntary methods fail." The very future of the United States was at risk. In spite or perhaps because of such language, the book was a best seller, as Malthus's had been. And this time too the bomb proved a dud. The green revolution—a combination of high-yield seeds, irrigation, pesticides, and fertilizers that enabled grain production to double —was already under way. Today many people are undernourished, but mass starvation is rare.

Ehrlich was right, though, that population would surge as medical science spared many lives. After World War II the developing countries got a sudden transfusion of preventive care, with the help of institutions like the World Health Organization and UNICEF. Penicillin, the smallpox vaccine, DDT (which, though later controversial, saved millions from dying of malaria)—all arrived at once. In India life expectancy went from 38 years in 1952 to 64 today; in China, from 41 to 73. Millions of people in developing countries who would have died in childhood survived to have children themselves. That's why the population explosion spread around the planet: because

When child mortality declines, couples eventually have fewer children—but that transition takes a generation.

a great many people were saved from dying.

And because, for a time, women kept giving birth at a high rate. In 18th-century Europe or early 20th-century Asia, when the average woman had six children, she was doing what it took to replace herself and her mate, because most of those children never reached adulthood. When child mortality declines, couples eventually have fewer children—but that transition usually takes a generation at the very least. Today in developed countries, an average of 2.1 births per woman would maintain a steady population; in the developing world, "replacement fertility" is somewhat higher. In the time it takes for the birthrate to settle into that new balance with the death rate, population explodes.

Demographers call this evolution the demographic transition. All countries go through it in their own time. It's a hallmark of human progress: In a country that has completed the transition, people have wrested from nature at least some control over death and birth. The global population explosion is an inevitable side effect, a huge one that some people are not sure our civilization can survive. But the growth rate was actually at its peak just as Ehrlich was sounding his alarm. By the early 1970s, fertility rates around the world had begun dropping faster

UNITED STATES Bundled newborns on September 1, 2010, are arranged for a portrait at Orlando's Winnie Palmer Hospital, the second busiest birth facility in the U.S. Unusual among industrial nations, the U.S. has a comparatively high fertility rate, due in part to the significant rate of teenage pregnancies and a steady influx of immigrants. By 2050 America's population is expected to top 400 million.

JOHN STANMEYER

than anyone had anticipated. Since then, the population growth rate has fallen by more than 40 percent.

THE FERTILITY DECLINE that is now sweeping the planet started at different times in different countries. France was one of the first. By the early 18th century, noblewomen at the French court were knowing carnal pleasures without bearing more than two children. They often relied on the same method Leeuwenhoek used for his studies: withdrawal, or coitus interruptus. Village parish records show the trend had spread to the peasantry by the late 18th century; by the end of the 19th, fertility in France had fallen to three children per woman—without the help of modern contraceptives. The key innovation was conceptual, not contraceptive, says Gilles Pison of the National Institute for Demographic Studies in Paris. Until the Enlightenment, "the number of children you had, it was God who decided. People couldn't fathom that it might be up to them."

Other countries in the West eventually followed France's lead. By the onset of World War II, fertility had fallen close to the replacement level in parts of Europe and the U.S. Then, after the surprising blip known as the baby boom, came the bust, again catching demographers off guard. They assumed some instinct would lead women to keep having enough children to ensure the survival of the species. Instead, in country after developed country, the fertility rate fell below replacement level. In the late 1990s in Europe it fell to 1.4. "The evidence I'm familiar with, which is anecdotal, is that women couldn't care less about replacing the species," Joel Cohen says.

The end of a baby boom can have two big economic effects on a country. The first is the "demographic dividend"—a blissful few decades when the boomers swell the labor force and the number of young and old dependents is relatively small, and there is thus a lot of money for other things. Then the second effect kicks in: The boomers start to retire. What had been

considered the enduring demographic order is revealed to be a party that has to end. The sharpening American debate over Social Security and last year's strikes in France over increasing the retirement age are responses to a problem that exists throughout the developed world: how to support an aging population. "In 2050 will there be enough people working to pay for pensions?" asks Frans Willekens, director of the Netherlands Interdisciplinary Demographic Institute in The Hague. "The answer is no."

In industrialized countries it took generations for fertility to fall to the replacement level or below. As that same transition takes place in the rest of the world, what has astonished demographers is how much faster it is happening there. Though its population continues to grow, China, home to a fifth of the world's people, is already below replacement fertility and has been for nearly 20 years, thanks in part to the coercive one-child policy implemented in 1979; Chinese women, who were bearing an average of six children each as recently as 1965, are now having around 1.5. In Iran, with the support of the Islamic regime, fertility has fallen more than 70 percent since the early '80s. In Catholic and democratic Brazil, women have reduced their fertility rate by half over the same quarter century. "We still don't understand why fertility has gone down so fast in so many societies, so many cultures and religions. It's just mind-boggling," says Hania Zlotnik, director of the UN Population Division.

"At this moment, much as I want to say there's still a problem of high fertility rates, it's only about 16 percent of the world population, mostly in Africa," says Zlotnik. South of the Sahara, fertility is still five children per woman; in Niger it is seven. But then, 17 of the countries in the region still have life expectancies of 50 or less; they have just begun the demographic transition. In most of the world, however, family size has shrunk dramatically. The UN projects that the world will reach replacement fertility by 2030. "The population as a whole is on a path toward nonexplosion—which is good news," Zlotnik says.

The bad news is that 2030 is two decades away and that the largest generation of adolescents in

---

Robert Kunzig is National Geographic's senior editor for the environment.

history will then be entering their childbearing years. Even if each of those women has only two children, population will coast upward under its own momentum for another quarter century. Is a train wreck in the offing, or will people then be able to live humanely and in a way that doesn't destroy their environment? One thing is certain: Close to one in six of them will live in India.

I HAVE UNDERSTOOD *the population explosion intellectually for a long time. I came to understand it emotionally one stinking hot night in Delhi a couple of years ago… The temperature was well over 100, and the air was a haze of dust and smoke. The streets seemed alive with people. People eating, people washing, people sleeping. People visiting, arguing, and screaming. People thrusting their hands through the taxi window, begging. People defecating and urinating. People clinging to buses. People herding animals. People, people, people, people.* —Paul Ehrlich

In 1966, when Ehrlich took that taxi ride, there were around half a billion Indians. There are 1.2 billion now. Delhi's population has increased even faster, to around 22 million, as people have flooded in from small towns and villages and crowded into sprawling shantytowns. Early last June in the stinking hot city, the summer monsoon had not yet arrived to wash the dust from the innumerable construction sites, which only added to the dust that blows in from the deserts of Rajasthan. On the new divided highways that funnel people into the unplanned city, oxcarts were heading the wrong way in the fast lane. Families of four cruised on motorbikes, the women's scarves flapping like vivid pennants, toddlers dangling from their arms. Families of a dozen or more sardined themselves into buzzing, bumblebee-colored auto rickshaws designed for two passengers. In the stalled traffic, amputees and wasted little children cried for alms. Delhi today is boomingly different from the city Ehrlich visited, and it is also very much the same.

At Lok Nayak Hospital, on the edge of the chaotic and densely peopled nest of lanes that is Old Delhi, a human tide flows through the

> China is already below replacement fertility, thanks in part to its coercive one-child policy.

entrance gate every morning and crowds inside on the lobby floor. "Who could see this and not be worried about the population of India?" a surgeon named Chandan Bortamuly asked one afternoon as he made his way toward his vasectomy clinic. "Population is our biggest problem." Removing the padlock from the clinic door, Bortamuly stepped into a small operating room. Inside, two men lay stretched out on examination tables, their testicles poking up through holes in the green sheets. A ceiling fan pushed cool air from two window units around the room.

Bortamuly is on the front lines of a battle that has been going on in India for nearly 60 years. In 1952, just five years after it gained independence from Britain, India became the first country to establish a policy for population control. Since then the government has repeatedly set ambitious goals—and repeatedly missed them by a mile. A national policy adopted in 2000 called for the country to reach the replacement fertility of 2.1 by 2010. That won't happen for at least another decade. In the UN's medium projection, India's population will rise to just over 1.6 billion people by 2050. "What's inevitable is that India is going to exceed the population of China by 2030," says A. R. Nanda, former head of the Population Foundation *(Continued on page 60)*

The Shape of Seven Billion

Each country in this cartogram is sized according to its projected population in 2011. Black dots represent the country's population in 1960; light dots are population added since then. Each dot represents two million people. Colors indicate the amount of growth (detailed below). Nations with populations under 1.5 million are not shown.

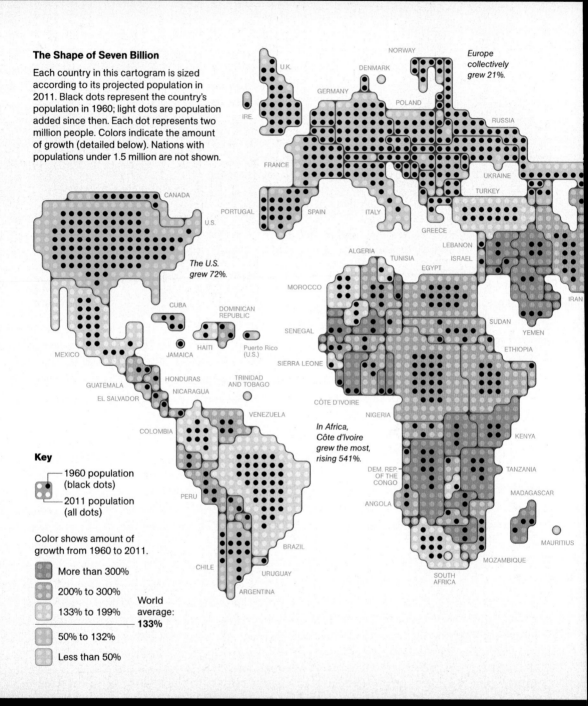

Europe collectively grew 21%.

The U.S. grew 72%.

In Africa, Côte d'Ivoire grew the most, rising 541%.

Key

- **1960 population** (black dots)
- **2011 population** (all dots)

Color shows amount of growth from 1960 to 2011.

- More than 300%
- 200% to 300%
- 133% to 199%
- 50% to 132%
- Less than 50%

World average: **133%**

There are more than twice as many people on the planet today as there were in 1960.

World population has never doubled this quickly before, but it is unlikely to double again. The era of explosive growth is expected to end by 2050, at more than 9 billion people, with an estimated range of 8 to 10.5 billion people.

World population

7 billion 2011

3 billion 1960

Youthful momentum

Age-distribution pyramids (right) show why the overwhelmingly young populations of developing countries will produce almost all the future population increase. Even with falling birthrates, the world's population is still growing by about 80 million people a year.

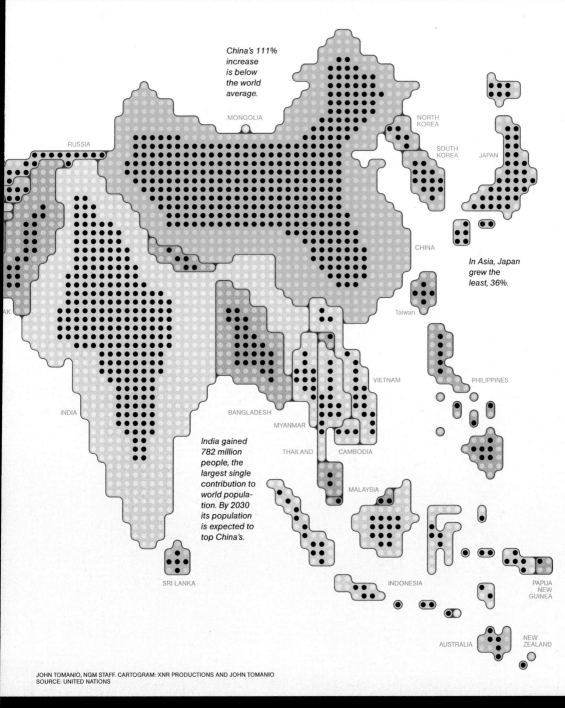

China's 111% increase is below the world average.

MONGOLIA

NORTH KOREA

SOUTH KOREA

JAPAN

RUSSIA

CHINA

In Asia, Japan grew the least, 36%.

Taiwan

VIETNAM

PHILIPPINES

INDIA

BANGLADESH

MYANMAR

THAILAND

CAMBODIA

MALAYSIA

India gained 782 million people, the largest single contribution to world population. By 2030 its population is expected to top China's.

SRI LANKA

INDONESIA

PAPUA NEW GUINEA

AUSTRALIA

NEW ZEALAND

AK.

PAK.

JOHN TOMANIO, NGM STAFF. CARTOGRAM: XNR PRODUCTIONS AND JOHN TOMANIO
SOURCE: UNITED NATIONS

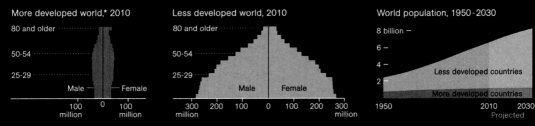

More developed world,* 2010

80 and older

50-54

25-29

Male — Female

100 million — 0 — 100 million

Less developed world, 2010

80 and older

50-54

25-29

Male — Female

300 200 100 0 100 200 300
million   million

World population, 1950-2030

8 billion —

6 —

4 —

2 —

Less developed countries

More developed countries

1950   2010   2030
                              Projected

CONSUMPTION

Wealthy nations use the most

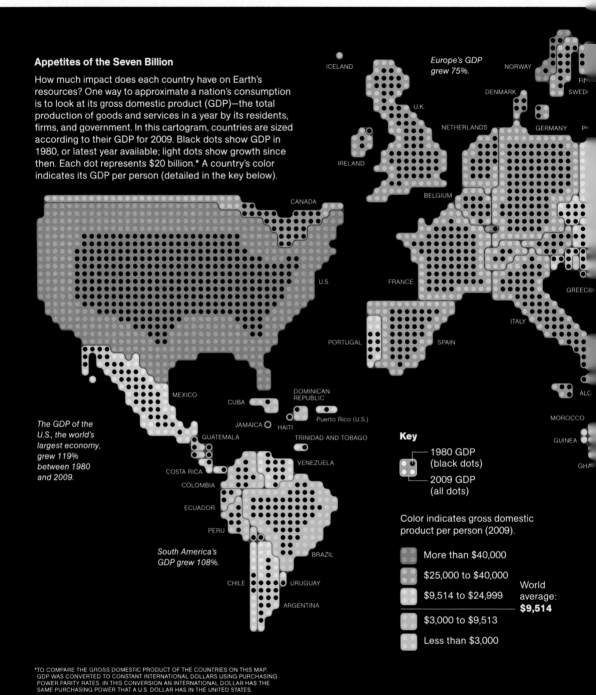

Appetites of the Seven Billion

How much impact does each country have on Earth's resources? One way to approximate a nation's consumption is to look at its gross domestic product (GDP)—the total production of goods and services in a year by its residents, firms, and government. In this cartogram, countries are sized according to their GDP for 2009. Black dots show GDP in 1980, or latest year available; light dots show growth since then. Each dot represents $20 billion.* A country's color indicates its GDP per person (detailed in the key below).

Europe's GDP grew 75%.

The GDP of the U.S., the world's largest economy, grew 119% between 1980 and 2009.

South America's GDP grew 108%.

ICELAND
NORWAY
FIN
DENMARK
SWED
U.K.
NETHERLANDS
GERMANY
P
IRELAND
BELGIUM
CANADA
FRANCE
GREEC
ITALY
U.S.
PORTUGAL
SPAIN
MEXICO
DOMINICAN REPUBLIC
CUBA
Puerto Rico (U.S.)
ALC
JAMAICA   HAITI
MOROCCO
GUATEMALA
TRINIDAD AND TOBAGO
GUINEA
COSTA RICA
VENEZUELA
GHA
COLOMBIA
ECUADOR
PERU
BRAZIL
CHILE   URUGUAY
ARGENTINA

Key

1980 GDP (black dots)
2009 GDP (all dots)

Color indicates gross domestic product per person (2009).

- More than $40,000
- $25,000 to $40,000
- $9,514 to $24,999 — World average: **$9,514**
- $3,000 to $9,513
- Less than $3,000

*TO COMPARE THE GROSS DOMESTIC PRODUCT OF THE COUNTRIES ON THIS MAP, GDP WAS CONVERTED TO CONSTANT INTERNATIONAL DOLLARS USING PURCHASING POWER PARITY RATES. IN THIS CONVERSION AN INTERNATIONAL DOLLAR HAS THE SAME PURCHASING POWER THAT A U.S. DOLLAR HAS IN THE UNITED STATES.

The world's gross domestic product* more than doubled from 1980 to 2009.

Economic development in China and India accounts for much of the recent rise and will continue to drive it. Global economic growth, and the improved standard of living it offers, means that resources are being consumed at record levels.

World GDP

$72.5 trillion 2009

$29.8 trillion 1980

Demand on natural resources will continue to increase.

Earth's finite resources will be stressed both by rising prosperity and sheer numbers of people (graphs, right). The consumption of resources now enjoyed in the wealthiest nations will be difficult to sustain worldwide.

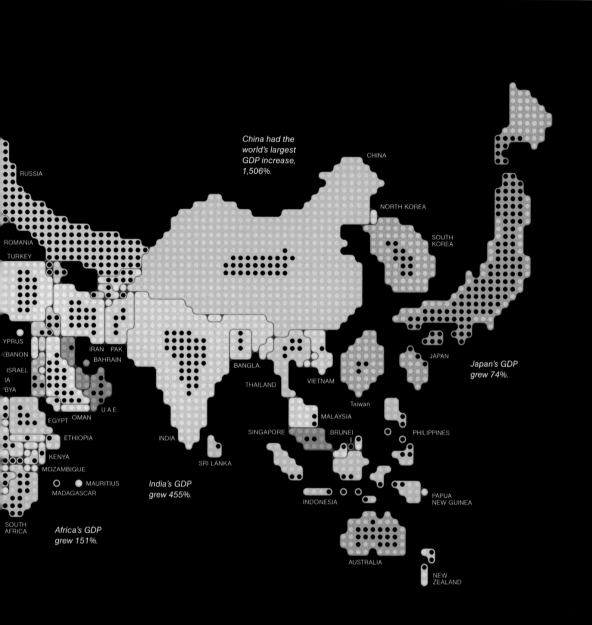

China had the world's largest GDP increase, 1,506%.

CHINA

NORTH KOREA

SOUTH KOREA

JAPAN

Japan's GDP grew 74%.

RUSSIA

ROMANIA
TURKEY

YPRUS
EBANON
ISRAEL
IA
BYA
EGYPT OMAN

IRAN PAK.
BAHRAIN
U.A.E.

BANGLA.

THAILAND

VIETNAM

Taiwan

MALAYSIA

SINGAPORE

BRUNEI

PHILIPPINES

ETHIOPIA

KENYA
MOZAMBIQUE

MAURITIUS
MADAGASCAR

INDIA

SRI LANKA

India's GDP grew 455%.

INDONESIA

PAPUA
NEW GUINEA

SOUTH
AFRICA

Africa's GDP grew 151%.

AUSTRALIA

NEW
ZEALAND

JOHN TOMANIO, NGM STAFF. CARTOGRAM: XNR PRODUCTIONS AND JOHN TOMANIO
SOURCES: WORLD BANK, CIA WORLD FACTBOOK, ECONSTATS (CARTOGRAM); UN (POPULATION
GRAPHIC); OXFORD FORECASTING (GDP GRAPHIC), U.S. ENERGY INFORMATION AGENCY (ENERGY
GRAPHIC; OECD IS THE ORGANISATION FOR ECONOMIC CO-OPERATION AND DEVELOPMENT)

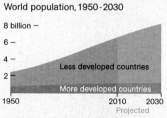

World population, 1950-2030

8 billion —

6 —

4 —

2 —

Less developed countries

More developed countries

1950   2010   2030
                              Projected

"MORE DEVELOPED" IS DEFINED IN THESE UN
STATISTICS AS THE U.S., CANADA, EUROPE, JAPAN,
AUSTRALIA, AND NEW ZEALAND.

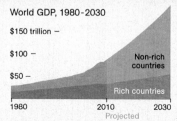

World GDP, 1980-2030

$150 trillion —

$100 —

$50 —

Non-rich
countries

Rich countries

1980   2010   2030
                              Projected

"RICH" INCLUDES THE UN'S MORE DEVELOPED COUNTRIES
PLUS CYPRUS, HONG KONG, ISRAEL, SINGAPORE,
SOUTH KOREA, AND TAIWAN.

World energy consumption, 2007-2030

Quadrillion BTUs

415

250   Low- to medium-income countries

246   High-income countries   271
       (OECD members)

2007   2015   2020   2025   2030
              Projected

OECD MEMBERS ARE THE UN'S MORE DEVELOPED
COUNTRIES PLUS CHILE, ISRAEL, MEXICO, SOUTH
KOREA, AND TURKEY.

FAMILY OF MANY

KENYA In a Nairobi slum Mary Wanza, a single mother earning three dollars a day, makes porridge for ten children, some hers, others grandkids and orphans. Wanza, 41, gave birth to the first of seven at age 15. Fertility rates remain high in sub-Saharan Africa; Kenya's rate fell from eight to five births per woman between 1960 and 2000 but has since declined only to 4.6. The global average is 2.5.

DOMINIC NAHR

TIME FOR ANOTHER GREEN REVOLUTION

CHINA Using every fertile inch, farmers harvest rice in the hills of Yunnan Province. High-yield seeds and ample fertilizer allow China to feed its billion-plus people on less than 10 percent of the Earth's arable land. Producing enough food as global population grows is possible, but doing so without exhausting finite resources, especially water, will be a challenge.

HIGH-TECH CAREGIVERS

JAPAN A talking robot helps 69-year-old Nabeshima Akiko shop in a test conducted by researchers from Keihanna Science City near Kyoto. Making up 23 percent of the population, the 29 million elderly in Japan far outnumber the young, an unprecedented situation that raises concerns about who—or what—will support the old in the years ahead.

RANDY OLSON

(Continued from page 49) of India, an advocacy group. "Nothing less than a huge catastrophe, nuclear or otherwise, can change that."

Sterilization is the dominant form of birth control in India today, and the vast majority of the procedures are performed on women. The government is trying to change that; a no-scalpel vasectomy costs far less and is easier on a man than a tubal ligation is on a woman. In the operating theater Bortamuly worked quickly. "They say the needle pricks like an ant bite," he explained, when the first patient flinched at the local anesthetic. "After that it's basically painless, bloodless surgery." Using the pointed tip of a forceps, Bortamuly made a tiny hole in the skin of the scrotum and pulled out an oxbow of white, stringy vas deferens—the sperm conduit from the patient's right testicle. He tied off both ends of the oxbow with fine black thread, snipped them, and pushed them back under the skin. In less than seven minutes—a nurse timed him—the patient was walking out without so much as a Band-Aid. The government will pay him an incentive fee of 1,100 rupees (around $25), a week's wages for a laborer.

The Indian government tried once before to push vasectomies, in the 1970s, when anxiety about the population bomb was at its height. Prime Minister Indira Gandhi and her son Sanjay used state-of-emergency powers to force a dramatic increase in sterilizations. From 1976 to 1977 the number of operations tripled, to more than eight million. Over six million of those were vasectomies. Family planning workers were pressured to meet quotas; in a few states, sterilization became a condition for receiving new housing or other government benefits. In some cases the police simply rounded up poor people and hauled them to sterilization camps.

The excesses gave the whole concept of family planning a bad name. "Successive governments refused to touch the subject," says Shailaja Chandra, former head of the National Population Stabilisation Fund (NPSF). Yet fertility in India has dropped anyway, though not as fast as in China, where it was nose-diving even before the draconian one-child policy took effect. The national average in India is now 2.6 children per woman, less than half what it was when Ehrlich visited. The southern half of the country and a few states in the northern half are already at replacement fertility or below.

In Kerala, on the southwest coast, investments in health and education helped fertility fall to 1.7. The key, demographers there say, is the female literacy rate: At around 90 percent, it's easily the highest in India. Girls who go to school start having children later than ones who don't. They are more open to contraception and more likely to understand their options.

SO FAR THIS APPROACH, held up as a model internationally, has not caught on in the poor states of northern India—in the "Hindi belt" that stretches across the country just south of Delhi. Nearly half of India's population growth is occurring in Rajasthan, Madhya Pradesh, Bihar, and Uttar Pradesh, where fertility rates still hover between three and four children per woman. More than half the women in the Hindi belt are illiterate, and many marry well before reaching the legal age of 18. They gain social status by bearing children—and usually don't stop until they have at least one son.

As an alternative to the Kerala model, some point to the southern state of Andhra Pradesh, where sterilization "camps"—temporary operating rooms often set up in schools—were introduced during the '70s and where sterilization rates have remained high as improved hospitals have replaced the camps. In a single decade beginning in the early 1990s, the fertility rate fell from around three to less than two. Unlike in Kerala, half of all women in Andhra Pradesh remain illiterate.

Amarjit Singh, the current executive director of the NPSF, calculates that if the four biggest states of the Hindi belt had followed the Andhra Pradesh model, they would have avoided 40 million births—and considerable suffering. "Because 40 million were born, 2.5 million children died," Singh says. He thinks if all India were to adopt high-quality programs to encourage sterilizations, in hospitals rather than camps, it could have

1.4 billion people in 2050 instead of 1.6 billion.

Critics of the Andhra Pradesh model, such as the Population Foundation's Nanda, say Indians need better health care, particularly in rural areas. They are against numerical targets that pressure government workers to sterilize people or cash incentives that distort a couple's choice of family size. "It's a private decision," Nanda says.

In Indian cities today, many couples are making the same choice as their counterparts in Europe or America. Sonalde Desai, a senior fellow at New Delhi's National Council of Applied Economic Research, introduced me to five working women in Delhi who were spending most of their salaries on private-school fees and after-school tutors; each had one or two children and was not planning to have more. In a nationwide survey of 41,554 households, Desai's team identified a small but growing vanguard of urban one-child families. "We were totally blown away at the emphasis parents were placing on their children," she says. "It suddenly makes you understand—that is why fertility is going down." Indian children on average are much better educated than their parents.

That's less true in the countryside. With Desai's team I went to Palanpur, a village in Uttar Pradesh—a Hindi-belt state with as many people as Brazil. Walking into the village we passed a cell phone tower but also rivulets of raw sewage running along the lanes of small brick houses. Under a mango tree, the keeper of the grove said he saw no reason to educate his three daughters. Under a neem tree in the center of the village, I asked a dozen farmers what would improve their lives most. "If we could get a little money, that would be wonderful," one joked.

The goal in India should not be reducing fertility or population, Almas Ali of the Population Foundation told me when I spoke to him a few days later. "The goal should be to make the villages livable," he said. "Whenever we talk of population in India, even today, what comes to our mind is the increasing numbers. And the numbers are looked at with fright. This phobia has penetrated the mind-set so much that all the focus is on reducing the number. The focus

People packed into slums need help, but the problem that needs solving is poverty, not overpopulation.

on people has been pushed to the background."

It was a four-hour drive back to Delhi from Palanpur, through the gathering night of a Sunday. We sat in traffic in one market town after another, each one hopping with activity that sometimes engulfed the car. As we came down a viaduct into Moradabad, I saw a man pushing a cart up the steep hill, piled with a load so large it blocked his view. I thought of Ehrlich's epiphany on his cab ride all those decades ago. People, people, people, people—yes. But also an overwhelming sense of energy, of striving, of aspiration.

THE ANNUAL MEETING of the Population Association of America (PAA) is one of the premier gatherings of the world's demographers. Last April the global population explosion was not on the agenda. "The problem has become a bit passé," Hervé Le Bras says. Demographers are generally confident that by the second half of this century we will be ending one unique era in history—the population explosion—and entering another, in which population will level out or even fall.

But will there be too many of us? At the PAA meeting, in the Dallas Hyatt Regency, I learned that the current population of the planet could fit into the state of Texas, if Texas were settled as densely as New York City. The comparison made me start thinking like Leeuwenhoek. If in 2045 there are nine billion people living on the six habitable continents, the world population density will be a little more than half that of France today. France is not usually considered a hellish place. Will the world be hellish then?

Some parts of it may well be; some parts of it are hellish today. There are now 21 cities with populations larger than ten million, and by 2050 there will be many more. Delhi adds hundreds of thousands of migrants each year, and those people arrive to find that "no plans have been made for water, sewage, or habitation," says Shailaja Chandra. Dhaka in Bangladesh and Kinshasa in the Democratic Republic of the Congo are 40 times larger today than they were in 1950. Their slums are filled with desperately poor people who have fled worse poverty in the countryside.

Whole countries today face population pressures that seem as insurmountable to us as India's did to Ehrlich in 1966. Bangladesh is among the most densely populated countries in the world and one of the most immediately threatened by climate change; rising seas could displace tens of millions of Bangladeshis. Rwanda is an equally alarming case. In his book *Collapse,* Jared Diamond argued that the genocidal massacre of some 800,000 Rwandans in 1994 was the result of several factors, not only ethnic hatred but also overpopulation—too many farmers dividing the same amount of land into increasingly small pieces that became inadequate to support a farmer's family. "Malthus's worst-case scenario may sometimes be realized," Diamond concluded.

Many people are justifiably worried that Malthus will finally be proved right on a global scale—that the planet won't be able to feed nine billion people. Lester Brown, founder of Worldwatch Institute and now head of the Earth Policy Institute in Washington, believes food shortages could cause a collapse of global civilization. Human beings are living off natural capital, Brown argues, eroding soil and depleting groundwater faster than they can be replenished. All of that will soon be cramping food production. Brown's Plan B to save civilization would put the whole world on a wartime footing, like the U.S. after Pearl Harbor, to stabilize climate and repair the ecological damage. "Filling the family planning gap may be the most urgent item on the global agenda," he writes, so if we don't hold the world's population to eight billion by reducing fertility, the death rate may increase instead.

Eight billion corresponds to the UN's lowest projection for 2050. In that optimistic scenario, Bangladesh has a fertility rate of 1.35 in 2050, but it still has 25 million more people than it does today. Rwanda's fertility rate also falls below the replacement level, but its population still rises to well over twice what it was before the genocide. If that's the optimistic scenario, one might argue, the future is indeed bleak.

But one can also draw a different conclusion—that fixating on population numbers is not the best way to confront the future. People packed into slums need help, but the problem that needs solving is poverty and lack of infrastructure, not overpopulation. Giving every woman access to family planning services is a good idea—"the one strategy that can make the biggest difference to women's lives," Chandra calls it. But the most aggressive population control program imaginable will not save Bangladesh from sea level rise, Rwanda from another genocide, or all of us from our enormous environmental problems.

Global warming is a good example. Carbon emissions from fossil fuels are growing fastest in China, thanks to its prolonged economic boom, but fertility there is already below replacement; not much more can be done to control population. Where population is growing fastest, in sub-Saharan Africa, emissions per person are only a few percent of what they are in the U.S.—so population control would have little effect on climate. Brian O'Neill of the National Center for Atmospheric Research has calculated that if the population were to reach 7.4 billion in 2050 instead of 8.9 billion, it would reduce emissions by 15 percent. "Those who say the whole problem is population are wrong," Joel Cohen says. "It's not even the dominant factor." To stop global warming we'll have to switch from fossil fuels to alternative energy—regardless of how big the population gets.

THE NUMBER OF PEOPLE DOES MATTER, of course. But how people consume resources matters a lot more. Some of us leave much bigger footprints than others. The central challenge for the future of people and the planet is how to raise more of us out of poverty—the slum dwellers in Delhi, the subsistence farmers in Rwanda—while reducing the impact each of us has on the planet.

The World Bank has predicted that by 2030 more than a billion people in the developing world will belong to the "global middle class," up from just 400 million in 2005. That's a good thing. But it will be a hard thing for the planet if those people are eating meat and driving gasoline-powered cars at the same rate as Americans now do. It's too late to keep the new middle class of 2030 from being born; it's not too late to change how they and the rest of us will produce and consume food and energy. "Eating less meat seems more reasonable to me than saying, 'Have fewer children!'" Le Bras says.

How many people can the Earth support? Cohen spent years reviewing all the research, from Leeuwenhoek on. "I wrote the book thinking I would answer the question," he says. "I found out it's unanswerable in the present state of knowledge." What he found instead was an enormous range of "political numbers, intended to persuade people" one way or the other.

For centuries population pessimists have hurled apocalyptic warnings at the congenital optimists, who believe in their bones that humanity will find ways to cope and even improve its lot. History, on the whole, has so far favored the optimists, but history is no certain guide to the future. Neither is science. It cannot predict the outcome of *People* v. *Planet*, because all the facts of the case—how many of us there will be and how we will live—depend on choices we have yet to make and ideas we have yet to have. We may, for example, says Cohen, "see to it that all children are nourished well enough to learn in school and are educated well enough to solve the problems they will face as adults." That would change the future significantly.

The debate was present at the creation of population alarmism, in the person of Rev.

> **It's too late to keep the new middle class of 2030 from being born. But it's not too late to change the ways we all consume.**

Thomas Malthus himself. Toward the end of the book in which he formulated the iron law by which unchecked population growth leads to famine, he declared that law a good thing: It gets us off our duffs. It leads us to conquer the world. Man, Malthus wrote, and he must have meant woman too, is "inert, sluggish, and averse from labour, unless compelled by necessity." But necessity, he added, gives hope:

"The exertions that men find it necessary to make, in order to support themselves or families, frequently awaken faculties that might otherwise have lain for ever dormant, and it has been commonly remarked that new and extraordinary situations generally create minds adequate to grapple with the difficulties in which they are involved."

Seven billion of us soon, nine billion in 2045. Let's hope that Malthus was right about our ingenuity. □

COMING IN MARCH How our massive impact on the planet is creating a new geologic epoch.

The Pulitzer Center on Crisis Reporting and PBS NewsHour join us in reporting on population issues throughout the year.

The magazine thanks the Wallace Global Fund and the members of the National Geographic Society for their generous support of this series of articles.

EMPTIED COUNTRYSIDE

RUSSIA Traffic is light—a horse cart with grain, a puppy in pursuit—on a road passing an abandoned granary and church in Novotishevoye, one of thousands of Russian villages depopulating as people move to cities and have fewer kids. To combat a low birthrate, the government has promised to pay $11,500 to women who have a second child.

RANDY OLSON

LAYING OUT THE AMERICAN DREAM

UNITED STATES A new house went up every 20 minutes during the 2004 building boom that seized Las Vegas and its sprawling suburbs, like Henderson. The American lifestyle—characterized by gas-thirsty cars and big houses using lots of electricity—contributes to the country's energy appetite; its carbon emissions are four times higher than the global average.

YANN ARTHUS-BERTRAND. ALTITUDE

LURE OF THE CITY

VENEZUELA Sharing a hillside with high-rise apartment dwellers, children dance at a shop in one of the squatter communities that ring Caracas, a city of three million. One in seven people on Earth lives in slums today. Providing them with better housing and education will be one of the great challenges facing a world of seven billion people and counting.

JONAS BENDIKSEN. MAGNUM PHOTOS

PHOENIX
RISING

After a rare bleaching disaster, the reefs
of the Phoenix Islands bounce back.

A green turtle glides over a wasteland of dead coral near Kanton island in the central Pacific. Before water temperatures spiked here in 2002-03, this reef was brimming with life.

On a mission to feed, yellowfin surgeonfish crowd the water at Nikumaroro. Although the atoll lost many corals, it kept an abundance of grazing fish that help reefs recover by keeping them clean.

Healthy new plate coral in the lagoon on Kanton island is a sign of hope. Since the waters here were hit by a severe bleaching episode, the coral has grown to a diameter of more than four feet.

By Gregory S. Stone

Photographs by Brian Skerry

The heavy iron anchor and chain tumbled noisily into the water. We lowered two red skiffs from our research vessel, loaded our diving gear, and sped off toward the lagoon. After a five-day sail from Fiji to Kanton island, we were anxious to see if reefs here had survived a rare ocean disaster—a lethal spike in the temperature of local seawater. During the El Niño of 2002-03, a body of water more than 1°C (1.8°F) warmer than usual had stalled for six months around the Phoenix Islands, a tiny archipelago in the central Pacific. We'd heard that the hot spot had severely bleached the region's corals. As I descended toward the lagoon floor, I was hoping things weren't as bad as we'd been told.

As I settled down beside the reef, I saw dead coral everywhere. What had been flourishing, overlapping, overflowing brown and auburn plates of corals were now ghostly, broken reminders of their former beauty. When I'd first visited the Phoenix Islands a decade ago, these reefs had supported numerous species of hard corals, as well as giant clams, sea anemones, nudibranchs, and great populations of fish, from blacktip reef sharks to parrotfish to bohar snappers. Because the islands have remained undisturbed for so long, they'd largely avoided overfishing, pollution, and other harmful impacts of modern civilization. But they hadn't been able to avoid climate change, which most scientists believe amplifies El Niños.

Not ready to accept this setback, I was heartened to see lots of reef fish and vibrant corals growing up through the rubble—early signs of recovery. Was it possible that the reefs of the Phoenix Islands, like their mythical namesake, were rising from the ashes of a terrible warming?

TEN YEARS AGO, I'd flown to Tarawa, capital of the Micronesian country of Kiribati, which includes the Phoenix Islands, to meet with government officials. At the time, the airport terminal was no bigger than a house, open-air with a thatched roof. I was met at the fisheries ministry by David Obura and Sangeeta Mangubhai

of CORDIO, an Indian Ocean conservation organization, who had helped me carry out the first systematic underwater surveys of the Phoenix Islands. An ancient air conditioner rattled away in the meeting room as we presented a slide show to the ministers of fisheries and environment, showing them scenes of sharks, flourishing coral, and dense clouds of colorful fish. Accustomed to the degraded reefs closer to their towns and villages, the ministers and their staff were as amazed as we had been at the "like new" reefs of the Phoenix Islands.

"Do you realize, Greg, that you're the first scientists who ever bothered to come tell us what they learned in our waters?" said Tetebo Nakara, then minister of fisheries.

During our subsequent talks with government officials, we found out that a fourth of Kiribati's income ($17 million in 2000) came from selling access to their reef fish, sharks, tunas, and other wild marine resources to nations such as Japan, South Korea, and the United States. In return for a commercial fishing license, a foreign company paid about 5 percent of the wholesale value of anything they took out of Kiribati waters.

I asked Nakara if Kiribati might consider receiving a payment in lieu of the access fees to leave the fish in the water. That way, it would receive badly needed income, but its underwater haven would be preserved. Without living reefs, these islands could rapidly erode. He smiled and said, "This could be good for Kiribati"—as long as his nation could keep receiving income from the "reverse fishing license." Anote Tong, Kiribati's president, enthusiastically backed the project and has since led it to fruition.

Formally declared a reserve at the 2006 Convention on Biological Diversity in Brazil, the Phoenix Islands Protected Area (PIPA) was expanded two years later to become what was then the world's largest marine protected area. At 157,000 square miles, it was nearly as big as California. But many questions remained: How could Kiribati put a fair price on its marine life? Where would the money come from? Who would police such a vast reserve?

To address such questions, I enlisted the

Frigatebird chicks await circling adults on Rawaki, one of 33 islands in the sprawling nation of Kiribati. Last year the Phoenix Islands Protected Area in Kiribati (map) became the largest World Heritage site.

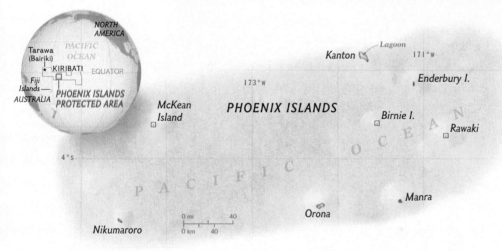

NORTH AMERICA

PACIFIC OCEAN

Tarawa (Bairiki)

KIRIBATI EQUATOR

Fiji Islands

AUSTRALIA PHOENIX ISLANDS PROTECTED AREA

Kanton — Lagoon — 171°W

173°W

McKean Island

PHOENIX ISLANDS

Enderbury I.

Birnie I.

Rawaki

4°S

PACIFIC OCEAN

Manra

0 mi 40
0 km 40

Orona

Nikumaroro

help of Conservation International (CI), which in 2001 had created the Global Conservation Fund to protect rain forest and other habitats through a similar strategy. Receptive to the idea, the Kiribati Parliament created the PIPA Conservation Trust with trustees from the New England Aquarium (NEA), CI, and the government of Kiribati, and fund-raising began for a $25-million endowment.

NOW I'D RETURNED to Kanton with David Obura and Randi Rotjan, a coral expert from NEA, and other scientists to assess the impact of the El Niño event. The bleaching had killed all the coral on the lagoon floor, but almost half appeared to be growing back—the fastest recovery any of us had ever seen. The reason seemed clear:

abundant fish. When coral bleaches, seaweed can grow out of control, stifling reef recovery. But fish eat the algae, keeping it from smothering the coral. Because fish populations had been protected here, the reefs remained surprisingly resilient even after suffering one of the worst bleaching events ever recorded.

As oceans continue to absorb the impacts of human activities and of climate change, we'll need more large protected areas like PIPA to help ecosystems survive. The oceans are our life-support system. There's never been a more important time to take care of them. □

Gregory S. Stone is chief scientist for oceans at Conservation International. Brian Skerry's photos of Japan's ocean wilderness appeared in November.

A school of Pacific steephead parrotfish (left) graze on dead coral at Kanton island. "You can hear them going *crunch, crunch, crunch,*" says Greg Stone, a diver and marine scientist. Because Kanton sits near the Equator, the island rarely experiences big shifts in meteorological conditions. But the El Niño of 2002-03 raised water temperatures here by more than 1°C (1.8°F) to as high as 88°F in some places, killing all the coral in the island's lagoon. Once coral dies, seaweed can take hold and grow on top of dead reefs, making resettlement by new coral difficult. That's where parrotfish come in: By grazing on algae, these and other herbivores keep the reef free of seaweed, enabling pink coralline algae to take hold and form a substrate for new coral. The four-saddle grouper (below) passes over the candy-pink algae on which new coral will grow.

Hovering briefly over the photographer, feet tucked up beneath its belly, a frigatebird comes in for a landing on Rawaki. Hundreds of thousands of birds lay their eggs on the island.

A shy and elusive fish, a Napoleon wrasse (right) at Orona island is a good omen for the marine reserve. Sought after by restaurants in China, Napoleon wrasses are typically fished out early when reefs are targeted. A 20-pound wrasse might be worth a thousand dollars in China. The fact that these fish are so abundant here means that the reef system is still relatively intact. Even without counting the vast open-ocean and largely unexplored deep-sea regions in the reserve, it shelters more than 800 fish, bird, and coral species, including 120 species of hard corals, such as the leafy formation (below) at Enderbury Island. Because of this, the reserve may serve as a model to restore reef systems elsewhere. "The Phoenix Islands are what the oceans were like a thousand years ago," scientist Stone says, "and what they can be like a thousand years from now."

The Telltale Scribes of Timbuktu

BY PETER GWIN   PHOTOGRAPHS BY BRENT STIRTON

*The caravan city harbors
great books, mysterious letters—
and a world of intrigue.*

A diagram of the Prophet's Mosque in Medina is one of the treasures found among thousands of ancient manuscripts.

A death in a prominent family draws a crowd of mourners. Their ranks include members of Timbuktu's three major ethnic groups: the Tuareg, Songhai, and Arabs. Each group has ruled the city during its long history.

In the ancient caravan city

of Timbuktu, many nights before I encountered the bibliophile or the marabout, or comforted the Green Beret's girlfriend, I was summoned to a rooftop to meet the salt merchant.

I had heard that he had information about a Frenchman who was being held by terrorists somewhere deep in the folds of Mali's northern desert. The merchant's trucks regularly crossed this desolate landscape, bringing supplies to the mines near the Algerian border and hauling the heavy slabs of salt back to Timbuktu. So it seemed possible that he knew something about the kidnappings that had all but dried up the tourist business in the legendary city.

I arrived at a house in an Arab neighborhood after the final call to prayer. A barefoot boy led the way through the dark courtyard and up a stone staircase to the roof terrace, where the salt merchant was seated on a cushion. He was a rotund figure but was dwarfed by a giant of a man sitting next to him who, when he unfolded his massive frame to greet me, stood nearly seven feet tall. His head was wrapped in a linen turban that covered all but his eyes, and his enormous warm hand enveloped mine.

We patiently exchanged pleasantries that for centuries have preceded conversations in Timbuktu. Peace be upon you. And also upon you. Your family is well? Your animals are fat? Your body is strong? Praise be to Allah. But after this prelude, the salt merchant remained silent. The giant produced a sheaf of parchment, and in a rich baritone slightly muffled by the turban over his mouth, he explained that it was a fragment of a Koran, which centuries ago arrived in the city via caravan from Medina. "Books," he said raising a massive index finger for emphasis, "were once more desired than gold or slaves in Timbuktu." He clicked a flashlight on and balanced a mangled pair of glasses on his nose. Gingerly turning the pages with his colossal fingers, he

Imam Chafi inspects his family's manuscripts, some over 400 years old, after rains collapsed his roof. Dozens of Timbuktu families receive aid to preserve their libraries, covering expenses such as roof repairs.

began to read in Arabic with the salt merchant translating: "Do men think they will be left alone on saying, 'We believe,' and that they will not be tested? We did test those before them, and Allah will certainly know those who are true from those who are false."

I wondered what this had to do with the Frenchman. "Notice how fine the script is," the giant said, indicating the delicate swirls of faded red and black ink on the yellowing page. He paused, "I will give it to you for a good price." At this point I fell into the excuses that I regularly used with the men and boys hawking silver jewelry near the mosque. I thanked him for showing me the book and told him that it was far too beautiful to leave Timbuktu. The giant nodded politely, gathered the parchment, and found his way down the stone stairs.

The salt merchant lit a cigarette. He had a habit of holding the smoke in his mouth until he spoke so that little puffs would tumble out along with his words. He explained that the giant

At its peak Timbuktu boasted 50,000 residents and streets swollen with arriving camel trains that stretched for miles. Today the city's population is about the same, but the caravans are almost extinct.

did not really want to sell the manuscript, which had been passed down through his mother's ancestors, but that his family needed the money. "He works for the guides, but there are no tourists," he said. "The problems in the desert are making all of us suffer." Finally, he mentioned the plight of the Frenchman. "I have heard the One-Eye has set a deadline."

During my time in Timbuktu, several locals denied that the city was unsafe and beseeched me to "tell the Europeans and Americans to come." But for much of the past decade the U.S. State Department and the foreign services of other Western governments have advised their citizens to avoid Timbuktu as well as the rest of northern Mali. The threats originate from a disparate collection of terrorist cells, rebel groups, and smuggling gangs that have exploited Mali's vast northern desert, a lawless wilderness three times the size of France and dominated by

Peter Gwin is a National Geographic *staff writer and a Pulitzer Center on Crisis Reporting grantee. Brent Stirton is on staff with Reportage by Getty Images.*

endless sand and rock, merciless heat and wind.

Most infamous among the groups is the one led by Mokhtar Belmokhtar, an Algerian leader of al Qaeda in the Islamic Maghreb (AQIM). Reputed to have lost an eye fighting the Russians in Afghanistan, he is known throughout the desert by his nom de guerre, Belaouer, Algerian-French slang for the One-Eye. Since 2003, his men have kidnapped 47 Westerners. Until 2009, AQIM had reached deals to release all of its hostages, but when the United Kingdom refused to meet the group's demands for Edwin Dyer, a British tourist, he was executed—locals say beheaded. His body was never found. In the weeks before my arrival, Belaouer and his cohorts had acquired a new inventory of hostages: three Spanish aid workers, an Italian couple, and the Frenchman.

"Belaouer is very clever," the salt merchant emphasized. He described how AQIM gained protection from the desert's Arab-speaking clans through Belaouer's marriage to the daughter of a powerful chief. One popular rumor describes him giving fuel and spare tires to a hapless

DESERT NEXUS

Founded as a seasonal camp by Tuareg herders, Timbuktu grew into a rich trading hub and by the 15th century had emerged as a center of Islamic learning. But as West African seaports grew, the caravans waned. By 1828, instead of a bustling, golden city, French explorer Réné Caillié found "a mass of ill-looking houses" and "the most profound silence."

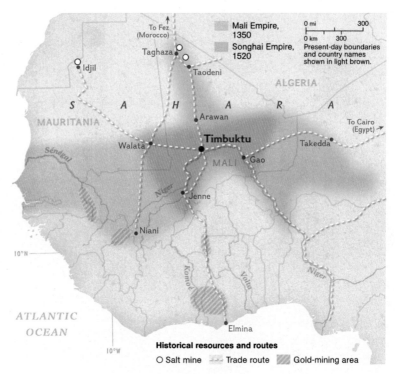

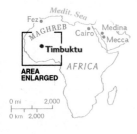

AREA
ENLARGED

0 mi   2,000
0 km   2,000

Historical resources and routes
○ Salt mine   --- Trade route   ▨ Gold-mining area

				MALI EMPIRE	SONGHAI EMPIRE			
600	**800**	**1100**	**1324**	**1500**	**1591**	**1612**	**1960**
Desert caravans link Mediterranean with African interior.	Arab merchants bring Islam to North Africa.	Timbuktu founded by Tuareg herders.	Emperor Musa travels to Mecca, orders mosque in Timbuktu.	Scholarship and trade flourish under Songhai Empire.	Moroccans invade and deport scholars.	Series of local rulers until French arrive 1894.	Mali gains independence from France.

Mali army patrol stranded in the desert. Such accounts have won him sympathizers among Timbuktu's minority Arab community, which in turn has angered the city's dominant ethnic groups, the Tuareg and Songhai.

Up on the roof the temperature had dropped. The salt merchant pulled a blanket around his shoulders and drew deeply on his cigarette. To the north, the city's lights gave way to the utter blackness of the open desert. He told me that the price AQIM had set for the Frenchman's life was freedom for four of its comrades arrested by Malian authorities last year. The deadline to meet these demands was four weeks away.

I asked him why the Mali army did not mount an offensive against the terrorists. He pointed the red ember of his cigarette toward a cluster of houses a few streets over and described how Belaouer's men had assassinated an army colonel in front of his young family in that

neighborhood a few months earlier. "Everyone in Timbuktu heard the shots," he said quietly. He mimicked the sound, *bang, bang, bang*. Then he waved the cigarette over the constellation of electric lights that revealed the shape of the city. "The One-Eye has eyes everywhere." And then, almost as an afterthought, he added, "I'm sure he knows you are here."

[*The Bibliophile*]

Sand blown in from the desert has nearly swallowed the paved road that runs through the heart of Timbuktu to Abdel Kader Haidara's home, reducing the asphalt to a wavy black serpent. Goats browse among trash strewn along the roadside in front of ramshackle mud-brick buildings. It isn't the prettiest city, an opinion that has been repeated by foreigners who have arrived with grand visions ever since 1828, when Réné Caillié became the first European to visit

MARGUERITE B. HUNSIKER AND JEROME N. COOKSON, NGM STAFF

With quills cut from desert shrubs, Boubacar Sadeck (in white) teaches calligraphy on the roof of his studio. The city once supported a flourishing industry of scribes who copied texts brought by traders and scholars.

Soldiers celebrate Malian independence day, September 22, but their revelry belies tensions beyond the city limits. Groups allied with al Qaeda hold hostages in the desert, crippling Timbuktu's tourism trade.

Timbuktu and return alive. Yet it is a watchful city: With every passing vehicle, children halt soccer games, women pause from stoking adobe ovens, and men in the market interrupt their conversations to note who is riding by. "It is important to know who is in the city," my driver said. Tourists and salt traders mean business opportunities; strangers could mean trouble.

I found Haidara, one of Timbuktu's preeminent historians, in the blinding mid-morning glare of his family's stone courtyard, not far

from the Sankore Mosque. He wanted to show me what he said was the first documentary evidence of democracy being practiced in Africa, a letter from an emissary to the sheikh of Masina. The temperature was quickly approaching 100°, and he sweated through his loose cotton robe as he moved dozens of dusty leather trunks, each containing a trove of manuscripts. He unbuckled the strap of a trunk, pried it open, and began carefully sorting the cracked leather volumes. I caught a pungent whiff of tanned

"Some of those words," he said triumphantly, "can only be found here in Timbuktu."

It is a practiced soliloquy but a logical point of view for a man whose family controls Timbuktu's largest private library, with some 22,000 manuscripts dating back to the 11th century and volumes of every description, some lavishly illuminated in gold and decorated with colorful marginalia. There are diaries filled with subterfuges and plots, as well as correspondence between sovereigns and their satraps, and myriad pages filled with Islamic theology, legal treatises, scientific notations, astrological readings, medicinal cures, Arabic grammar, poetry, proverbs, and magic spells. Among them are also the little scraps of paper that track the mundanities of commerce: receipts for goods, a trader's census of his camel herd, inventories of caravans. Most are written in Arabic, but some are in Haidara's native Songhai. Others are written in Tamashek, the Tuareg language. He can spend hours sitting among the piles, dipping into one tome after another, each a miniature telescope allowing him to peer backward in time.

The mosaic of Timbuktu that emerges from his and the city's other manuscripts depicts an entrepôt made immensely wealthy by its position at the intersection of two critical trade arteries—the Saharan caravan routes and the Niger River. Merchants brought cloth, spices, and salt from places as far afield as Granada, Cairo, and Mecca to trade for gold, ivory, and slaves from the African interior. As its wealth grew, the city erected grand mosques, attracting scholars who, in turn, formed academies and imported books from throughout the Islamic world. As a result, fragments of the Arabian Nights, Moorish love poetry, and Koranic commentaries from Mecca mingled with narratives of court intrigues and military adventures of mighty African kingdoms.

As new books arrived, armies of scribes copied elaborate facsimiles for the private libraries of local teachers and their wealthy patrons. "You see?" said Haidara, twirling his hand with a flourish. "Books gave birth to new books."

Timbuktu's downfall came when one of its

skins and mildew. "Not in here," he muttered.

Haidara is a man obsessed with the written word. Books, he said, are ingrained in his soul, and books, he is convinced, will save Timbuktu. Words form the sinew and muscle that hold societies upright, he argued. Consider the Koran, the Bible, the American Constitution, but also letters from fathers to sons, last wills, blessings, curses. Thousands upon thousands of words infused with the full spectrum of emotions fill in the nooks and corners of human life.

Keeping an eye out for hippos, dockworkers bathe next to a boat in the Niger River, some six miles south of Timbuktu. The Niger once brought slaves and gold to the city; now it brings food, diesel fuel, and tourists.

MERCHANTS BROUGHT CLOTH, SPICES, AND SALT FROM

conquerors valued knowledge as much as its own residents did. The city never had much of an army of its own. After the Tuareg founded it as a seasonal camp about A.D. 1100, the city passed through the hands of various rulers—the Malians, the Songhai, the Fulani of Masina. Timbuktu's merchants generally bought off their new masters, who were mostly interested in the rich taxes collected from trade. But when the Moroccan army arrived in 1591, its soldiers looted the libraries and rounded up the most accomplished scholars, sending them back to the Moroccan sultan. This event spurred the great dispersal of the Timbuktu libraries. The remaining collections were scattered among the families who owned them. Some were sealed inside the mud-brick walls of homes; some were buried in the desert; many were lost or destroyed in transit.

It was Haidara's insatiable love for books that first led him to follow his ancestors into a career as an Islamic scholar and later propelled him into the vanguard of Timbuktu's effort to save the city's manuscripts. Thanks to donations

from governments and private institutions around the world, three new state-of-the-art libraries have been constructed to collect, restore, and digitize Timbuktu's manuscripts. Haidara heads one of these new facilities, backed by the Ford Foundation, which houses much of his family's vast collection. News of the manuscript revival prompted the Aga Khan, an important Shiite Muslim leader, to restore one of the city's historic mosques and Libyan leader Muammar Qaddafi to begin building an extravagant walled resort in anticipation of future academic congresses.

I asked Haidara if the problems in the desert are impeding Timbuktu's renaissance. "Criminals, or whoever else it may be, are the least of my worries," he said, pointing to pages riddled with tiny oblong holes. "Termites are my biggest enemies." Scholars estimate many thousands of manuscripts lie buried in the desert or forgotten in hiding places, slowly succumbing to heat, rot, and bugs. The question of what might be lost haunts Haidara. "In my

A mechanic repairs a truck used to carry slabs of salt from mines deep in the Sahara. Camel trains still work the route, but trucks haul more and make the 900-mile round trip in 10 days versus 45 for camels.

FAR AFIELD TO TRADE FOR GOLD, IVORY, AND SLAVES.

worst dreams," he said, "I see a rare text that I haven't read being slowly eaten."

[*The Marabout*]

After the salt merchant's talk about the One-Eye, a local man suggested I consult a certain marabout, a type of Muslim holy man. For a price, he could provide me with a gris-gris, a small leather pouch containing a verse from the Koran imbued by the marabout with a protective spell. "He is the only one who can truly protect you from Belaouer," the man had confided.

Arriving at the marabout's house, I entered a small anteroom where a thin, bedraggled man was crouching on the dirt floor. He reached out and firmly held one of my hands in both of his. A few of his fingernails had grown long and curved off the tips of his fingers like talons. "Peace upon you," the man cried out. But after I returned his greeting, he didn't let go of my hand. Instead he sat on the ground, rocking slightly back and forth, firmly holding on, and smiling up at me. Then I noticed a chain

fastened around his ankle. It snaked across the floor to an iron ring embedded in the stone wall.

The marabout, a balding man in his late 40s, who wore reading glasses on a string around his neck, appeared. He politely explained that the chained man was undergoing a process that would free him from spirits that clouded his mind. "It is a 30-day treatment," he said. He reached out and gently stroked the crouching man's hair. "He is already much better than he was when he arrived."

The marabout led the way to his sanctum, and my translator and I followed him across a courtyard, passing a woman and three children who sat transfixed in front of a battered television blaring a Pakistani game show. We ducked through a bright green curtain into a tiny airless room piled with books and smelling of incense and human sweat. The marabout motioned us to sit on a carpet. Gathering his robes, he knelt across from us and produced a matchstick, which he promptly snapped into three pieces. He held them up so that I could see that they

High heels and high hopes have become vogue among teenage girls at Timbuktu's lone high school. A rise in female pupils, aided by scholarships, marks a national effort to cut Mali's 74 percent illiteracy rate.

Conservators at the Mamma Haidara Library, Timbuktu's largest private manuscript collection, repair pages using paper fabricated to match the originals. The texts are digitized, then sealed in acid-free boxes.

MANY THOUSANDS OF MANUSCRIPTS LIE BURIED IN THE

were indeed broken and then rolled up the pieces in the hem of his robe. With a practiced flourish worthy of any sleight-of-hand expert, he unfurled the garment and revealed the matchstick, now unbroken. His powers, he said, had healed it. My translator excitedly tapped my knee. "You see," he said, "he is a very powerful marabout." As if on cue, applause erupted from the game show in the courtyard.

The marabout retrieved a palm-size book bound with intricately tooled leather. The withered pages had fallen out of the spine, and he gently turned the brittle leaves one by one until he found a chart filled with strange symbols. He explained that the book contained spells for everything from cures for blindness to charms guaranteed to spark romance. He looked up from the book. "Do you need a wife?" I said that I already had one. "Do you need another?"

I asked if I could examine the book, but he refused to let me touch it. Over several years his uncle had tutored him in the book's contents, gradually opening its secrets. It contained powers

that, like forces of nature, had to be respected. He explained that his ancestors had brought the book with them when they fled Andalusia in the 15th century after the Spanish defeated the Moors. They had settled in Mauritania, and he had only recently moved from there with his family. "I heard the people of Timbuktu were not satisfied with the marabouts here," he said. I asked who his best customers were. "Women," he answered, grinning, "who want children."

He produced a small calculator, punched in some numbers, and quoted a price of more than a thousand dollars for the gris-gris. "With it you can walk across the entire desert and no one will harm you," he promised.

[The Green Beret's Girlfriend]

The young woman appeared among the jacaranda trees of the garden café wearing tight jeans and a pink T-shirt. She smiled nervously, and I understood how the Green Beret had fallen for her. Aisha (not her real name) was 23 years old, petite, with a slender figure. She worked as

A rare 17th-century Tuareg manuscript contains an illustration of the Prophet's sandals. Over the years many such tomes have been sold on the black market and spirited out of Mali.

DESERT, SLOWLY SUCCUMBING TO HEAT, ROT, AND BUGS.

a waitress. Her jet black skin was unblemished except for delicate ritual scars near her temples, which drew attention to her large, catlike eyes.

We met across from the Flame of Peace, a monument built from some 3,000 guns burned and encased in concrete. It commemorates the 1996 accord that ended the rebellion waged by Tuareg and Arabs against the government, the last time outright war visited Timbuktu.

Aisha pulled five tightly folded pieces of paper from her purse and laid them on the table next to a photograph of a Caucasian man with a toothy smile. He appeared to be in his 30s and was wearing a royal blue Arab-style robe and an indigo turban. "That is David," she said, lightly brushing a bit of sand from the photo.

They had met in December 2006, when the U.S. had sent a Special Forces team to train Malian soldiers to fight AQIM. David had seen her walking down the street and remarked to his local interpreter how beautiful she was. The interpreter arranged an introduction, and soon the rugged American soldier and the Malian

beauty were meeting for picnics on the sand dunes ringing the city and driving to the Niger River to watch the hippos gather in the shallows. Tears welled in Aisha's eyes as she recounted these dates. She paused to wipe her face. "He only spoke a little French," she said, laughing at the memory of their awkward communication.

Aisha's parents also came from starkly different cultures. Her mother's ancestors were Songhai, among the intellectuals who helped create Timbuktu's scholarly tradition. Her father, a Fulani, descended from the fierce jihadis who seized power in the early 1800s and imposed sharia in Timbuktu. In Aisha's mind, her relationship with David continued a long tradition of mingling cultures. Many people pass through Timbuktu, she said. "Who is to say who Allah brings together?"

Two weeks after the couple met, David asked her to come to the United States. He wanted her to bring her two-year-old son from a previous relationship and start a life together. When her family heard the news, her uncle told David that since Aisha was Muslim, he would have to convert if he wanted to marry her. To his surprise, David agreed.

Three nights before Christmas, David left the Special Forces compound after curfew and met one of Aisha's brothers, who drove him through the dark, twisting streets to the home of an imam. Through an interpreter the imam instructed the American to kneel facing Mecca and recite the *shahadah* three times: "There is no God but Allah, and Muhammad is his prophet." He gave the soldier a Koran and instructed him to pray five times a day and to seek Allah's path for his life.

When David returned to the compound, his superiors were waiting for him. They confined him to quarters for violating security rules. Over the next week, he was not allowed to mix with the other Green Berets nor permitted to see Aisha, but he was able to smuggle out three letters. One begins: "My dearest [Aisha], Peace be upon you. I love you. I am a Muslim. I am very happy that I have been shown the road to Allah, and I wouldn't have done it without meeting you. I think Allah brought me here to you..." He continues: "I am not to leave the American house. But this does not matter. The Americans cannot keep me from Allah, nor stop my love for you. *Allahu Akbar*. I will return to the States on Friday."

Aisha never saw him again. He sent two emails from the United States. In the last message she received from him, he told her that the Army was sending him to Iraq and that he was afraid of what might happen. She continued to email him, but after a month or so her notes began bouncing back.

As she spoke, Aisha noticed tears had fallen onto the letters. She smoothed them into the paper and then carefully folded up the documents. She said she would continue to wait for David to send for her. "He lives in North Carolina," she said, and the way she pronounced North Carolina in French made me think she imagined it to be a distant and exotic land.

I tried to lighten her mood, teasing that she had better be careful or Abdel Kader Haidara

would hear of her letters. After all, they are Timbuktu manuscripts, and he will want them for his library. She wiped her eyes once more. "If I can have David, he can have the letters."

[*Uncertain Endings*]

A month after I left Timbuktu, Mali officials, under pressure from the French government, freed four AQIM suspects in exchange for the Frenchman. The Italian couple was released, as were the Spanish aid workers after their

Dawn finds boys at a religious school studying the words of the Koran inscribed on their slates. "Reading, writing, and the Koran," says their teacher, echoing ages of Timbuktu scholars, "these are important."

government reportedly paid a large ransom. Since then AQIM has kidnapped six other French citizens. One was executed. At press time five remained in captivity somewhere in the desert. The marabout and his family disappeared from their home. Rumor spread that he had been recruited by the One-Eye to be his personal marabout.

I emailed David, who was serving in Iraq and is no longer in the Special Forces. He wrote back a few days later. "That time was extremely difficult for me, and it still haunts me." He added, "I haven't forgotten the people I met there, quite the contrary, I think of them often."

I called Aisha and told her that he was still alive. That was months ago. I haven't heard any more from David, but Aisha still calls, asking if there is any news. Sometimes her voice is drowned out by the rumble of the salt trucks; sometimes I hear children playing or the call to prayer. At times Aisha cries on the phone, but I have no answers for the girl from Timbuktu. □

A giant cave column swagged in flowstone towers over explorers swimming through the depths of Hang Ken, one of 20 new caves discovered last year in Vietnam.

CONQUERING AN
INFINITE CAVE

There's a jungle inside Vietnam's mammoth cavern.
A skyscraper could fit too. And the end is out of sight.

A half-mile block of 40-story buildings could
fit inside this lit stretch of Hang Son Doong,
which may be the world's biggest subterranean passage. In nearby Loong Con (left),
a climber ascends a shaft of sunlight.

A jungle inside a cave? A roof collapse long ago in Hang Son Doong let in light; plants thickly followed. As "Sweeny" Sewell climbs to the surface, hikers struggle through the wryly named Garden of Edam.

BY MARK JENKINS

PHOTOGRAPHS BY CARSTEN PETER

"Past the hand of dog, watch out for dinosaurs,"
says a voice in the dark.

I recognize Jonathan Sims's clipped, British military accent but have no idea what he's talking about. My headlamp finds him, gray muttonchops curling out from beneath his battered helmet, sitting alone in the blackness along the wall of the cave.

"Carry on mate," growls Sims. "Just resting a buggered ankle."

The two of us have roped across the thundering, subterranean Rao Thuong River and climbed up through 20-foot blades of limestone to a bank of sand. I continue alone, following the beam of my headlamp along year-old footprints.

In the spring of 2009, Sims was a member of the first expedition to enter Hang Son Doong, or "mountain river cave," in a remote part of central Vietnam. Hidden in rugged Phong Nha-Ke Bang National Park near the border with Laos, the cave is part of a network of 150 or so caves, many still not surveyed, in the Annamite Mountains. During the first expedition, the team explored two and a half miles of Hang Son Doong before a 200-foot wall of muddy calcite stopped them. They named it the Great Wall of Vietnam. Above it they could make out an open space and traces of light, but they had no idea what lay on the other side. A year later, they have returned—seven hard-core British cavers, a few scientists, and a crew of porters—to climb the wall, if they can, measure the passage, and push on, if possible, all the way to the end of the cave.

The trail disappears before me into a difficult pile of breakdown—building-size blocks of stone that have fallen from the ceiling and crashed onto the cave floor. I crane my head back, but the immensity of the cave douses my headlamp's tiny light, as if I were staring up into a starless night sky. I've been told I'm inside a space large enough to park a 747, but I have no way to know; the darkness is like a sleeping bag pulled over my head.

I switch off my headlamp just to feel the depth of the darkness. At first there is nothing. But

then, as my pupils adjust, I'm surprised to make out a faint, ghostly light ahead. I pick my way through the rubble, almost running from excitement, rocks scattering beneath my feet and echoing in the invisible chamber. Traversing up a steep slope, I turn a ridge as if on a mountainside and am stopped in my tracks.

An enormous shaft of sunlight plunges into the cave like a waterfall. The hole in the ceiling through which the light cascades is unbelievably large, at least 300 feet across. The light, penetrating deep into the cave, reveals for the first time the mind-blowing proportions of Hang Son

Mist sweeps past the hills of Phong Nha-Ke Bang National Park, its 330 square miles set aside in 2001 to protect one of Asia's largest cave systems. During the Vietnam War, North Vietnamese soldiers hid in caves from U.S. air strikes. Bomb craters now serve as fishponds.

Moss-slick boulders and a 30-foot drop test author Mark Jenkins at the forest-shrouded entrance to Hang Son Doong. "Even though these caves are huge, they're practically invisible until you're right in front of them," Jenkins says. Hunters have found caves by spotting winds gusting from underground openings.

Doong. The passage is perhaps 300 feet wide, the ceiling nearly 800 feet tall: room enough for an entire New York City block of 40-story buildings. There are actually wispy clouds up near the ceiling.

The light beaming from above reveals a tower of calcite on the cave floor that is more than 200 feet tall, smothered by ferns, palms, and other jungle plants. Stalactites hang around the edges of the massive skylight like petrified icicles. Vines dangle hundreds of feet from the surface; swifts are diving and cutting in the brilliant column of sunshine. The tableau could have been created by an artist imagining how the world looked millions of years ago.

Mark Jenkins is a contributing writer for the magazine. Carsten Peter last photographed Mexico's Cave of Crystals for our November 2008 issue.

Jonathan Sims catches up with me. Between us and the sunlit passage ahead stands a stalagmite that in profile resembles the paw of a dog.

"The Hand of God would be just too corny," he says, pointing at the formation. "But the Hand of Dog does nicely, don't you think?"

He clicks off his headlamp and unweights his gimpy ankle.

"When we first got to the collapsed doline, that skylight up there, I was with another caver and we both had four-year-old sons, so we were experts on dinosaurs, and the whole scene reminded us of something right out of Sir Arthur Conan Doyle's novel *The Lost World*," he says. "When my partner went exploring forward into the sunlight, I told him to 'watch out for dinosaurs,' and the name stuck."

Two decades ago, the leaders of this expedition, Howard Limbert and his wife, Deb, became

Were the six-inch screws to pop out,
the rope would lose its anchor and he'd plummet to his death.

Dubbed the Great Wall of Vietnam, a 200-foot cliff halted the advance of the first team to enter Hang Son Doong, in 2009. When explorers returned, Sewell drilled bolts for climbers to scale the obstacle with ropes. A white streak below, to his right, marks how high water rises during the wet season.

the first cavers to visit Vietnam since the 1970s. Back then, the country's caves were legendary but unexplored. In 1941 Ho Chi Minh had planned his revolution against the Japanese and French in Pac Bo Cave north of Hanoi, and during the Vietnam War thousands of Vietnamese hid from American bombing raids inside caves. The Limberts, experienced cavers from the Yorkshire dales of northern England, made contact with the University of Science in Hanoi and, after obtaining sheaves of permits, mounted an expedition in 1990. They've made 13 trips since, not only discovering one of the longest river caves in the world—12-mile Hang Khe Ry, not far from Son Doong—but also helping the Vietnamese create 330-square-mile Phong Nha-Ke Bang National Park, which now attracts a quarter million Vietnamese and foreign visitors a year. Tourists, who dramatically increase the income of local villagers, come to see the park's namesake show cave, Hang Phong Nha, which workers light up like a psychedelic rock concert.

Because of the dense jungle, the Limberts might never have found the caves without help from area residents. "Mr. Khanh has been with us from the beginning," Howard says, nodding toward a thin man smoking a cigarette beside the campfire. We're squatting around the fire just inside the entrance to Hang En, the mile-long portal that tunnels beneath a ring of mountains into the lost world. "Couldn't have done it without him," Howard says. Ho Khanh's family lived in a nearby village. His father was killed in the war, forcing Khanh at a young age to fend for himself in the jungle. For years he hunted all over this border country, taking refuge in caves when it rained, or rained bombs.

"It took three expeditions to find Hang Son

PATH OF A RIVER CAVE

In April 2009 a British-Vietnamese team began exploring Hang Son Doong, or "mountain river cave" (below). Beneath the rain forest along the Vietnam-Laos border they discovered a cavernous limestone passage more than 2.5 miles long and in places over 600 feet high, carved by a subterranean river two to five million years ago. Expeditions have found more than 150 caves in this area since 1990, mapping nearly 90 miles of passages.

A MEGA-SINKHOLE OPENS

The cave's Garden of Edam sinkhole owes its size to its location: Another passage entered the main cave here. When the ceiling collapsed at this junction, it opened a pit 1,500 feet deep, with a 650-foot-wide opening.

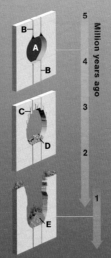

Million years ago

Dissolving
2 million to 5 million years ago
A subterranean chamber (**A**) forms as water flowing along fracture lines (**B**) dissolves the limestone.

Expanding
With continued erosion and collapse (**C**), debris accumulates faster than it can be removed by the flowing water (**D**).

Collapse and colonization
Within the past million years
The chamber's roof collapses, opening the cave to the sky. Ferns and trees colonize the exposed debris cone (**E**).

South entrance
Flowing into the cave, the Rao Thuong River soon vanishes into the limestone. High water makes exploration too dangerous in summer's rainy season.

Watch Out for Dinosaurs
The whimsically named sinkhole lets in light and rain, which seeps into the river now carving new passages beneath the cave floor.

1,400 ft —
1,200 —
1,000 —
800 —
600 —
400 —
200 —
0 —

Viewpoint of photo p.114

South entrance discovered in 2009

Empire State Building at same scale for comparison

Dark section of passage

Hand of Dog

pp.108-109

p.124

pp.118-119

1 mile —

MARTIN GAMACHE, NGM STAFF. ART: BRYAN CHRISTIE
SOURCES: GEOLOGICAL SURVEY OF VIETNAM; DARRYL GRANGER, PURDUE UNIVERSITY; NGUYEN HIEU, HANOI UNIVERSITY OF SCIENCE; HOWARD LIMBERT, PETER MACNAB, ROBBIE SHONE, AND TONY WALTHAM, BRITISH CAVE RESEARCH ASSOCIATION

CANVAS FOR CAVES

Vast formations of lime-
stone, in places thousands
of feet thick, were depos-
ited across this region 250
to 350 million years ago.
Tectonic action uplifted and
fractured the rock. Rivers
followed these fractures
underground, dissolving
networks of cave passages.

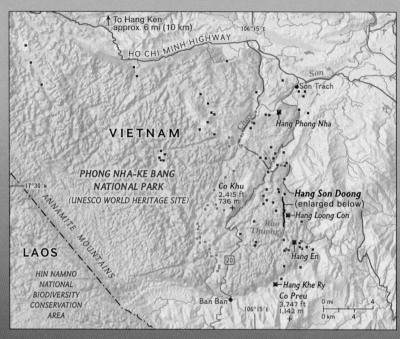

To Hang Ken
approx. 6 mi (10 km)

106°15' E

HO CHI MINH HIGHWAY

Son
Son Trach

Chay

Hang Phong Nha

VIETNAM

17°30' N

PHONG NHA-KE BANG
NATIONAL PARK
(UNESCO WORLD HERITAGE SITE)

Co Khu
2,415 ft
736 m

Hang Son Doong
(enlarged below)
Hang Loong Con

LAOS

Rao
Thuong

ANNAMITE MOUNTAINS

20

Hang En

HIN NAMNO
NATIONAL
BIODIVERSITY
CONSERVATION
AREA

Hang Khe Ry
Co Preu
3,747 ft
1,142 m

Ban Ban

106°15' E

0 mi   4

0 km   4

VIETNAM
Hanoi ★

PHONG NHA-KE BANG
NATIONAL PARK

ASIA
VIETNAM

Ho Chi
Minh City
(Saigon)

Networks of caves
Vom caves   Phong Nha caves   Other caves   Limestone extent

Two drainage systems, the Vom and the Phong Nha, channel subterranean waters
that have carved two namesake cave networks.

Garden of Edam
In the larger and
older of the cave's
two sinkholes, a forest
of 100-foot trees
covers an 850-foot-
tall debris cone.

Dark passages
With light entering the
relatively straight cave
through its entrances
and sinkholes, only a
few stretches lie in
pitch darkness.

Great Wall of Vietnam
Scaling this calcite wall,
cavers found a north
entrance in 2010. The
muddy maze called Pass-
chendaele is watered by
an internally rising stream.

pp.
110-111 Cross section
above left

p. 115

Passchendaele

Pearl
Harbor

North
entrance
discovered
in 2010

North

2 miles

Navigating an algae-skinned maze, expedition organizers Deb and Howard Limbert lead the way across a sculpted cavescape in Hang Son Doong. Ribs form as calcite-rich water overflows pools.

Hang Son Doong's airy chambers sprout life where light enters from above—a different world from the bare, cramped, pitch-black spaces familiar to most cavers. Ferns and other greenery colonize rimstone (above). In the jungles directly beneath roof openings, explorers have seen monkeys, snakes, and birds.

Doong," Howard says. "Khanh had found the entrance as a boy but had forgotten where it was. He only found it again last year."

Stands of bamboo and other vegetation cover mounds of limestone here, making the place all but impenetrable. Below the surface, this part of Vietnam is one immense limestone block, says Darryl Granger, a geomorphologist from Purdue University. "The whole region was squeezed upward when the Indian subcontinent smashed into the Eurasian continent 40 to 50 million years ago," he says. Hang Son Doong was formed two to five million years ago, when river water flowing across the limestone burrowed down along a fault, scouring out a giant tunnel beneath the mountains. In places where the limestone was weak, the ceiling collapsed into sinkholes, creating the gigantic skylights.

Anette Becher, a German caver and biologist,

has found wood lice, fish, and millipedes inside the cave that are all white, which is common for creatures that live in the dark. And Dai Inh Vu, a botanist from the Vietnam Academy of Science and Technology, has identified the plants growing beneath the skylights, finding basically the same mix that grows in the forest above. But such science on the run is not the real focus of this expedition, whose central purpose is exploration. For cavers like the Limberts, discovering a cave as big as Hang Son Doong is like finding a previously unknown Mount Everest underground. "We've just scratched the surface here," Howard says of the national park, which was named a World Heritage site in 2003 for its forests and caves. "There is so much more to do."

When Howard and Deb first saw these enormous spaces, they felt certain they had discovered

Some cave pearls are the size of baseballs, larger than any the cavers have ever seen.

Rare cave pearls, most of them dime-size here, fill dried-out terrace pools near the Garden of Edam in Hang Son Doong. This unusually large collection of stone spheres formed drip by drip over the centuries as calcite crystals left behind by water layered themselves around grains of sand, enlarging over time.

the largest cave in the world—and they might be right. There are longer caves than Hang Son Doong—the Mammoth Cave system in Kentucky, with 367 total miles, holds that record. There are deeper caves too—Krubera-Voronja, the "crow's cave," plunges 7,188 feet in the western Caucasus Mountains of Georgia. But for giant passages, there are few caves that can compare. At the time of the Limberts' discovery of Hang Son Doong, the largest passage was thought to be Deer Cave in Malaysian Borneo's Gunung Mulu National Park, which was recently surveyed at 1.2 miles long, 500 feet wide, and 400 feet tall. But as the explorers would eventually determine, using precise laser instruments, Hang Son Doong is more than 2.5 miles long with a continuous passage as wide as 300 feet and, in places, over 600 feet high.

"We weren't actually searching for the largest

cave in the world," Deb says. But she's thrilled that the cave's newfound fame might improve the lives of local villagers.

After five days of hiking, hauling, and crawling, the expedition is still only halfway into the cave. Counting all the cavers, scientists, a film and photography crew, and porters, we are a team of more than two dozen, which seems to have slowed us down. Besides that, the going gets dangerous as we climb through the breakdown in Watch Out for Dinosaurs: One misstep on slick boulders could mean a fall of more than a hundred feet.

When we reach the next skylight, the Garden of Edam (another cheesy pun), it's even bigger than the first, almost as wide as the roof of the Superdome in New Orleans. Below the opening is another mountain of breakdown with a jungle of hundred-foot-tall trees, lianas, and burning

In the dry season, from November to April, a caver can safely explore Hang Ken, with its shallow pools. Come the monsoon, the underground river swells and floods the passages, making the cave impassable.

Like a castle on a knoll, a rock formation shines beneath a skylight in Hang Son Doong. A storm had just filled the pool, signaling that exploring season was coming to an end.

nettles. As our time and supplies begin to run out, Howard decides the moment has come to send an advance team ahead to the Great Wall of Vietnam, to see if an assault is really possible.

The wall lies more than a mile away at the end of a corridor shaped like a V with a foot-deep trench of water at the bottom. Mud walls, sticky as peanut butter, rise 40 feet high on either side. It is not possible to walk in the trench, only to stumble. By the time you reach the wall, you're so covered in mud you appear to have gone swimming in chocolate pudding. The cavers named this passage Passchendaele, after the trench warfare battle of World War I in which the Allies lost 310,000 soldiers to gain only five miles of ground near the Belgian village of Ypres.

Climbing an overhanging 200-foot-tall wall of mud is technical, risky business, so you need just the right type of madmen. Luckily, Howard has handpicked Gareth "Sweeny" Sewell and Howard Clarke for the advance team. The two have been caving together for 20 years in the nastiest potholes in England. Clarky is a bull semen salesman, and Sweeny is a legal specialist who somehow convinced his wife that they should sell their one and only car so he could keep heading off on caving expeditions.

The first day at the base of the wall, as Clarky belays, Sweeny begins boldly working his way upward, drilling hole after hole. Almost all of the holes are too hollow to hold a screw from which to hang their ropes.

For 12 hours they jabber in their expletive-laden Yorkshire vernacular—"ez bloody crap covered wit mood," Sweeny says at one point. Neither says a word about the true dangers of the task. Were any of the six-inch screws to pop out, the rope Sweeny is hanging on would lose its anchor and he'd likely zipper the rest of the screws and plummet to his death.

On the second day of the climb, after bivouacking at the bottom of the wall for the night, Sweeny returns to his previous high point, with Clarky belaying again. Soon enough the whirring of his drill echoes through the domed blackness, Sweeny so high up we can see only the glimmer of his headlamp. At two in the afternoon—

of course it doesn't matter a bit what time it is when it's dark 24/7—after 20 hours of drilling holes and climbing higher, Sweeny finally disappears over the wall and some minutes later we hear: *"AAIIOOOOO!!"*

Clarky ascends the rope next, then yells down for me, the words bouncing through the cave: "Well, ye comin' up or wat!"

At the top of the Great Wall of Vietnam we can literally see light at the end of the tunnel and start howling our heads off. The rest of the expedition will later tell us that they actually heard our hallos more than a mile away in the cave. Measurements made at the top of the wall will reveal that from the bottom of Passchendaele to the ceiling is 654 feet. It's just the three of us now, exploring. No human has ever been here before. We drop down off the backside of the Great Wall and begin ascending a staircase of rock toward the exit.

"Will ye look at deese!" roars Clarky, kneeling beside a dried-up pool. Sweeny and I gather around. Inside the pool, illuminated by our headlamps, are cave pearls.

Cave pearls are formed when a drop of water from the ceiling hits the limestone floor and throws up a speck of rock. This grain is jostled in its little cup of stone every time a drop hits it. Over thousands of years, a solid, almost perfectly round calcite pearl is formed.

Pearls are rare and in most caves are no larger than a marble. The cave pearls here are the size of baseballs, larger than any the cavers have ever seen. (Their preternatural size may be due to the enormous distance the ceiling waterdrops fall.)

"I 'ereby christen this passage Pearl 'arbor," Clarky announces.

Twenty more minutes and we're scrambling up and out of the cave. It is raining in the jungle. We hack our way far enough out into the forest to recognize a horizon and determine that this is not just another skylight, but that we have discovered the end of Hang Son Doong. Sweeny and Clarky are far too humble to openly express that we've just completed the first push through what is very likely the largest cave passage in the world. ☐

CAHOKIA

AMERICA'S FORGOTTEN CITY

Four centuries before Columbus arrived in the Americas, Indians in Illinois created a city with up to 15,000 inhabitants, more than a hundred earthen mounds, and far-reaching influence. What was this place we call Cahokia, and what happened to it?

DON BURMEISTER

BIRDMAN TABLET, A.D. 1250–1350; CAHOKIA MOUNDS STATE HISTORIC SITE, ILLINOIS

Spirits and shamans loomed large in Cahokia and other mound-building communities, as revealed by a ceremonial mask and a stone tablet (left). The shell beads surrounding the tablet were found in a burial mound containing human sacrifices.

A few miles from Cahokia in St. Louis, residents saw the city's many mounds as little more than handy sources of soil. The largest, Big Mound, stood some 30 feet high and 300 feet long and took years to level. Oblivious to its historical value, workers needing fill dirt for a railroad bed carted off the last of it in 1869.

BY GLENN HODGES

PHOTOGRAPHS BY DON BURMEISTER AND IRA BLOCK

If they ever build a Wal-Mart at Machu Picchu, I will think of Collinsville Road.

I'm standing at the center of what was once the greatest civilization between the deserts of Mexico and the North American Arctic—America's first city and arguably American Indians' finest achievement—and I just can't get past the four-lane gash that cuts through this historic site. Instead of imagining the thousands of people who once teemed on the grand plaza here, I keep returning to the fact that Cahokia Mounds in Illinois is one of only eight cultural World Heritage sites in the United States, and it's got a billboard for Joe's Carpet King smack in the middle of it.

But I suppose Cahokia is lucky. Less than ten miles to the west, the ancient Indian mounds that gave St. Louis the nickname Mound City in the 1800s were almost completely leveled by the turn of the century. Today only one survives, along with some photographs and a little dog-leg road named Mound Street. The relentless development of the 20th century took its own toll on Cahokia: Horseradish farmers razed its second biggest mound for fill in 1931, and the site has variously been home to a gambling hall, a housing subdivision, an airfield, and (adding insult to injury) a pornographic drive-in. But most of its central features survived, and nearly all of those survivors are now protected. Cahokia Mounds may not be aesthetically pristine, but at 4,000 acres (2,200 of which are preserved as a state historic site), it is the largest archaeological site in the United States, and it has changed our picture of what Indian life was like on this continent before Europeans arrived.

Cahokia was the apogee, and perhaps the origin, of what anthropologists call Mississippian culture—a collection of agricultural communities that reached across the American Midwest and Southeast starting before A.D. 1000 and peaking around the 13th century. The idea that American Indians could have built something resembling a city was so foreign to European

A ten-story behemoth known as Monks Mound is the center-piece of the 2,200-acre Cahokia Mounds State Historic Site. Eighty surviving mounds dot this cultural World Heritage site; some were used as building platforms, some for burials.

IRA BLOCK

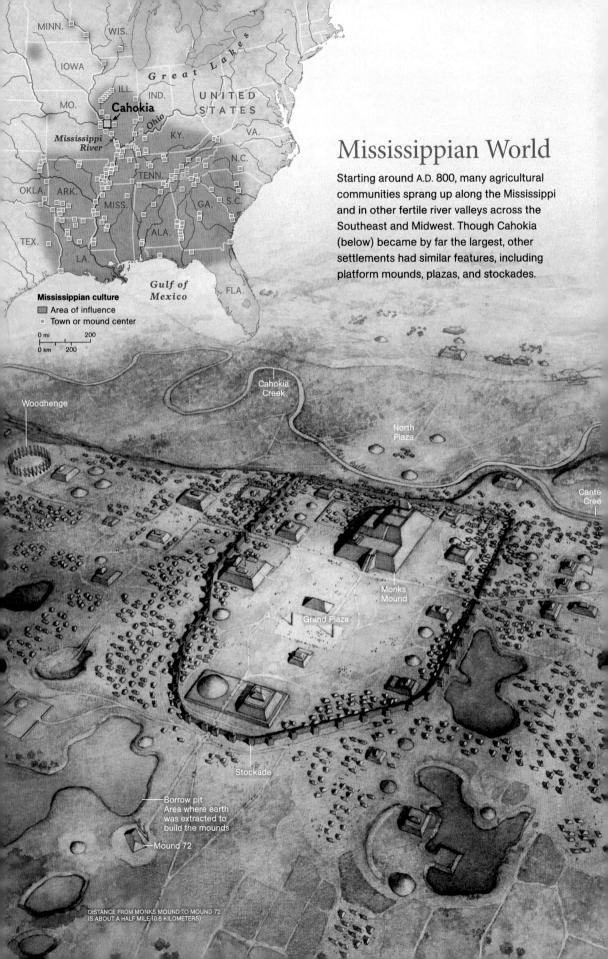

MINN. WIS.

IOWA

ILL. IND. UNITED STATES

MO. **Cahokia** Ohio KY. VA.

Mississippi River TENN. N.C.

OKLA. ARK. MISS. GA. S.C.

TEX. ALA.

LA. *Gulf of Mexico* FLA.

Mississippian culture
◼ Area of influence
◻ Town or mound center

0 mi 200
0 km 200

Mississippi World

Starting around A.D. 800, many agricultural communities sprang up along the Mississippi and in other fertile river valleys across the Southeast and Midwest. Though Cahokia (below) became by far the largest, other settlements had similar features, including platform mounds, plazas, and stockades.

Woodhenge

Cahokia Creek

North Plaza

Canté Cree

Monks Mound

Grand Plaza

Stockade

Borrow pit
Area where earth was extracted to build the mounds

Mound 72

DISTANCE FROM MONKS MOUND TO MOUND 72
IS ABOUT A HALF MILE (0.8 KILOMETERS)

settlers, that when they encountered the mounds of Cahokia—the largest of which is a ten-story earthen colossus composed of more than 22 million cubic feet of soil—they commonly thought they must have been the work of a foreign civilization: Phoenicians or Vikings or perhaps a lost tribe of Israel. Even now, the idea of an Indian city runs so contrary to American notions of Indian life that we can't seem to absorb it, and perhaps it's this cognitive dissonance that has led us to collectively ignore Cahokia's very existence. Have you ever heard of Cahokia? In casual conversation, I've found almost no one outside the St. Louis area who has.

Our ignorance has deep roots. The first person to write a detailed account of Cahokia's mounds was Henry Brackenridge, a lawyer and amateur historian who came upon the site and its massive central mound while exploring the surrounding prairie in 1811. "I was struck with a degree of astonishment, not unlike that which is experienced in contemplating the Egyptian pyramids," he wrote. "What a stupendous pile of earth! To heap up such a mass must have required years, and the labors of thousands." But newspaper accounts of his discovery were widely ignored. He complained of this in a letter to his friend former President Thomas Jefferson, and with friends in such high places, word of Cahokia did eventually get around. Unfortunately it was not word most Americans, including subsequent Presidents, were very interested in hearing. The United States was trying to get Indians out of the way, not appreciate their history. Andrew Jackson's Indian Removal Act of 1830, which ordered the relocation of eastern Indians to land west of the Mississippi, was premised on the idea that Indians were nomadic savages who couldn't make good use of land anyway. Evidence of an ancient Indian city—one that rivaled the size of Washington, D.C., at the time—would have mucked up the story line.

Even American universities took scant notice

Author Glenn Hodges is a former staff writer for National Geographic. Photographers Ira Block and Don Burmeister are based in New York City.

The whole city seemed to spring to life almost overnight around 1050, a phenomenon now referred to as a "big bang."

of Cahokia and other homegrown sites before the second half of the 20th century. They preferred sending their archaeologists to Greece and Mexico and Egypt, where the stories of ancient civilizations were comfortably distant and romantic. The few people who championed Cahokia and its neighboring mound centers at East St. Louis and St. Louis fought a mostly losing battle against development and neglect for the better part of a century. The latter two sites—among the largest Mississippian communities in their own right—were destroyed and paved over. And though Monks Mound, named for French monks who once lived in its shadow, became a tiny state park in 1925, it was used for sledding and Easter egg hunts. The rest of Cahokia was largely ignored—built on and only sporadically studied—until the 1960s.

And that's when history demonstrated its fine sense of irony, because the biggest construction project to tear into Cahokia would also put it on the map. President Dwight Eisenhower's interstate highway program, though a massive undertaking that changed America's landscape as dramatically as the railroads once did, contained provisions for the study of archaeological sites in its path. This meant more money for excavations than had ever been available, as well as a clear agenda for where to dig, when, and how fast. With two highways slated to skewer the ancient city—I-55/70 now bisects Cahokia's north plaza, creating a road sandwich with Collinsville Road, a quarter mile to the south—archaeologists began to systematically study the site. What they found was nothing less than revelatory.

It became apparent that Cahokia was more

JEROME COOKSON, MARIEL FURLONG, AND AMANDA HOBBS, NGM STAFF. ART AND MAP: GREG HARLIN
SOURCES: BILL ISEMINGER AND MARK ESAREY, CAHOKIA MOUNDS STATE HISTORIC SITE; JOHN KELLY, WASHINGTON UNIVERSITY IN ST. LOUIS

CAHOKIA   135

Placid in the morning mist, the plazas surrounding Monks Mound teemed with thousands during construction, which required 15 million baskets of soil. A large temple or palace was built on top, perhaps serving as center stage for religious ceremonies.
DON BURMEISTER

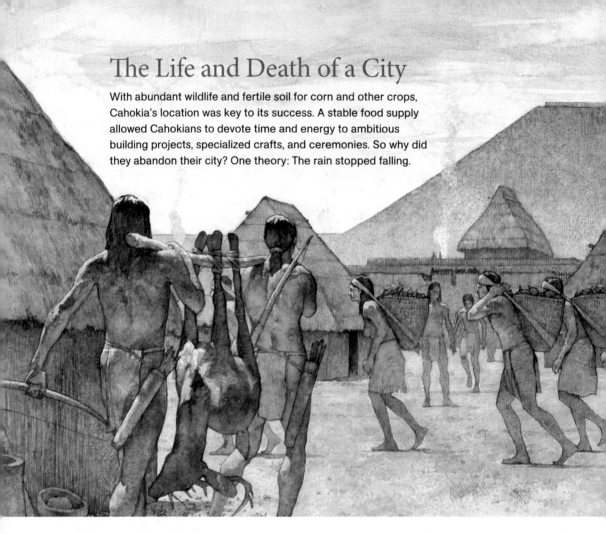

The Life and Death of a City

With abundant wildlife and fertile soil for corn and other crops, Cahokia's location was key to its success. A stable food supply allowed Cahokians to devote time and energy to ambitious building projects, specialized crafts, and ceremonies. So why did they abandon their city? One theory: The rain stopped falling.

than just a stupendous pile of earth or a ceremonial site where scattered tribes congregated once in a while. Nearly everywhere they dug, archaeologists found homes—indicating that thousands of people had once lived in the community—and many of these homes had been built within a very brief span of time. In fact, the whole city seemed to spring to life almost overnight around 1050, a phenomenon now referred to as a "big bang." People streamed in from surrounding areas, built houses, and quickly constructed the infrastructure of a new city—including several mounds with buildings on top and a grand plaza the size of 45 football fields, used for everything from sporting events to communal feasts to religious celebrations.

Making the story even more interesting was the clear evidence of ritual human sacrifice. Archaeologists excavating Mound 72, as they labeled it, found the remains of 53 women and one very high status man, as well as the decapitated remains of four men who may have been on the wrong side of some sort of authority. The discovery belied the common belief that American Indians lived in egalitarian communities without the sorts of often brutally maintained hierarchies that defined many other civilizations. Was Cahokia an empire, like the Mesoamerican civilizations to the south? It was too soon to tell, but something spectacular had happened here, and it became clear this was a mystery worth trying to solve.

IF YOU WANT TO UNDERSTAND Cahokia, the first thing you've got to do is climb the 156 steps to the top of Monks Mound. From the flat top of this colossus—with a footprint of 14 acres, it is larger at its base than the Great Pyramid of Khufu, Egypt's largest—you not only get a sense of how much labor went into its construction, but you can also understand why it might have been built in the first place. From here you can survey Cahokia's domain: the vast floodplain known as the American Bottom, stretching from St. Louis to a long line of bluffs three miles east

of Cahokia and as far to the north and south as the eye can see. After directing the construction of what would have been the highest geographic feature in the 175-square-mile floodplain, a chief or high priest would have had a bird's-eye view of the land under his sway.

Of course, that scenario presumes we know that Cahokia had such a single leader, which we don't. We don't even know what this place was called—the name Cahokia is borrowed from a tribe that lived nearby in the 1600s—or what the people who lived here called themselves. With no written language, they left behind the same scattering of meager clues that makes understanding prehistoric societies everywhere so challenging. (Pottery's fine and everything, but how much would a foreign culture really learn about us by looking at our dishes?) If deciphering the story of history is contentious, try coming to agreement on the story of prehistory. "You know what they say," says Bill Iseminger, an archaeologist who has worked at Cahokia for 40

years. "Put three archaeologists in a room and you get five opinions."

He's not exaggerating much. Even when Cahokia scholars agree, they tend to frame their positions so it seems like they're disagreeing—but there are points of general consensus. Everyone agrees that Cahokia developed quickly a couple centuries after corn became an important part of the local diet, that it drew together people from the American Bottom, and that it dwarfed other Mississippian communities in size and scope. The battle lines tend to form along the questions of how populous it was, how centralized its political authority and economic organization were, and the nature and extent of its reach and influence.

At one extreme you have descriptions of Cahokia as a "theater of power," a hegemonic empire sustained by force that reached deep into the Mississippian world and perhaps connected to Mesoamerican civilizations such as the Maya or Toltec. At the other extreme you have

MARIEL FURLONG AND AMANDA HOBBS, NGM STAFF. ART: GREG HARLIN
SOURCES: BILL ISEMINGER AND MARK ESAREY, CAHOKIA MOUNDS STATE HISTORIC SITE; JOHN KELLY, WASHINGTON UNIVERSITY IN ST. LOUIS

CHUNKEY PLAYER EFFIGY PIPE, 1250-1350; MUSKOGEE COUNTY, OKLAHOMA

CHUNKEY STONES, 1050-1200; CAHOKIA MOUNDS, ILLINOIS

SHELL GORGET, 1250-1350; CASTALIAN SPRINGS MOUND, TENNESSEE

MOTHER EFFIGY BOTTLE, 1250-1350; EAST ST. LOUIS, ILLINOIS

COPPER REPOUSSÉ PLAQUE, 1200-1400; DUNKLIN COUNTY, MISSOURI

Artifacts from Cahokia and elsewhere reveal a broad network of trade in goods and raw materials, including copper from the Great Lakes region (above) and shells from the Gulf of Mexico (bottom, far left). Chunkey, a popular sport using rolling stones (top, left), was played throughout the Mississippian region.

Cahokia was a ghost town by the time Columbus landed. Its demise is perhaps an even greater mystery than its emergence.

characterizations of Cahokia as little more than an especially large Mississippian town whose residents had a talent for making big piles of dirt. But as usual, most of the action happens in the middle area between those poles.

Right now the discussion is being spearheaded by Tim Pauketat at the University of Illinois, who with his colleague Tom Emerson argues that Cahokia's big bang was the product of a visionary moment: A leader, prophet, or group cast a vision for a new way of living that attracted people from far and near, creating a rapidly expanding cultural movement.

When I meet Pauketat at Cahokia to see the site through his eyes, he's more interested in showing me what he's found in the uplands several miles to the east: signs that Cahokians held sway over outlying laborer communities that supplied food to the city and its elites—evidence, Pauketat argues, that Cahokia's political economy was centralized and broad reaching. This is a controversial theory, because the research supporting it hasn't been published yet, and because it goes to the heart of the argument about just what kind of society Cahokia was.

Gayle Fritz at Washington University in St. Louis says that if Cahokia was a city, it wasn't the kind we usually think of, but one full of farmers growing their own food in nearby fields. Otherwise there would be more signs of storage facilities. It's this sort of practical limit on the size of a subsistence-based agricultural community that leads minimalists like Penn State's George Milner to argue that population estimates for Cahokia—currently ranging between 10,000 and 15,000 for the city proper and

another 20,000 to 30,000 in the surrounding areas—are inflated by a factor of two or more and that characterizations of Cahokia as something like a protostate are way off base. But with less than one percent of Cahokia excavated, speculation by every camp remains in higher supply than evidence. Washington University's John Kelly, a longtime stalwart of Cahokian archaeology, sums up the present understanding of Cahokia nicely: "People aren't really sure what it is."

Nor do people know what happened to it. Cahokia was a ghost town by the time Columbus landed in the New World, and the American Bottom and substantial parts of the Mississippi and Ohio River Valleys were so depopulated they are referred to as the Vacant Quarter. Cahokia's demise is perhaps an even greater mystery than its emergence, but there are a few clues. The city grew to prominence during an especially favorable climate phase and began shrinking around the time the climate became cooler, drier, and less predictable. For an agricultural community dependent on regular crop yields, the changing conditions could have been anything from stressful to catastrophic.

The fact that between 1175 and 1275 Cahokia's inhabitants built—and rebuilt, several times—a stockade encircling the main part of the city suggests that conflict or the threat of conflict had become a standard feature of life in the region, perhaps because there were fewer resources. Furthermore, dense populations create environmental problems as a matter of course—deforestation, erosion, pollution, disease—that can be difficult to counter and that have been the downfall of many a society.

That Cahokia lasted for only some 300 years, and was at the peak of its power for half that at most, should not come as a surprise. "If you

A cobblestone memorial in north St. Louis (bottom) marks the site of Big Mound, which until the mid-1800s was one of the largest Indian burial mounds in the United States. Photographs of its destruction (top) later helped fuel a movement to save Cahokia's mounds from a similar fate.

THOMAS M. EASTERLY, MISSOURI HISTORY MUSEUM

DON BURMEISTER

The last Indian mound in St. Louis finally has a guardian. After a year on the market, Sugar Loaf Mound was bought by the Osage, one of several tribes who claim Cahokians as ancestors. Their plan: Remove the house and restore a memory.

DON BURMEISTER

look broadly at human history, failure is the norm," says Tom Emerson. "What's amazing is when things last."

Emerson is currently heading a huge excavation in East St. Louis of Cahokia's next-door neighbor, a site that had thousands of residents of its own (sort of like Fort Worth to Cahokia's Dallas). And again, road construction is paying the tab: A new bridge across the Mississippi is giving Emerson's team a crack at 36 acres that had been lost to earlier progress, if you can call the twisted path of human history something as simple as "progress." The stockyards that were built on the ruins of this Mississippian settlement have been shuttered for years, casualties of East St. Louis's own decline from a vibrant city to a collection of vacant lots and boarded-up buildings. This is history's march in our own midst: fleet of foot and easy to miss.

When I drive to St. Louis to see if anything still memorializes the big mound (named, with an appropriate lack of imagination, Big Mound) that was destroyed there by 1869, I'm surprised to see that the exact spot where it was located is where the new bridge from East St. Louis will land. I ask around and learn that archaeologists excavated this lot too before construction started. But they didn't find a trace of Big Mound, only remnants of the 19th-century factories that had taken its place. That is now the accessible history of this site. The rest is gone.

After a failed first attempt, I do finally locate a marker for Big Mound. It's a little cobblestone memorial a half block down Broadway from Mound Street, with a missing plaque and grass growing between its rocks. As luck would have it, I find it just as a man arrives to spray it with weed killer. I ask him if he works for the city, and he says no. His name is Gary Zigrang, and he owns a building down the block. He's called the city about the marker's disrepair, and they haven't done anything, so he's taking matters into his own hands. And as he sprays the weeds on the forgotten memorial for the forgotten mound of the forgotten people who once lived here, he says, "What a shame. There's history here, and it needs to be taken care of." ☐

Carsten Peter climbs in Hang Son Doong.

ON ASSIGNMENT **Getting the Hang of It** Shooting in Vietnam's massive Hang Son Doong posed some problems for photographer Carsten Peter. Climbing up ropes from the cold of the cave floor into the warmer, more humid layers of air above caused condensation to form on his cameras. "The only thing you can do is wait," he says, for the equipment to warm and the moisture to dissipate. But waiting for hours while dangling from a rope is problematic as well. "You lose the circulation in your legs, so you have to do a little moving around and stretching on the rope. This gear is not really made to be comfortable." Learn more about the Hang Son Doong expedition by tuning in to *World's Biggest Cave* on the Nat Geo Channel on December 20 at 10 p.m.

NG BOOKS **Thrive** Best-selling author Dan Buettner knows a thing or two about the world's happiest, healthiest people. He has written about them and their longevity for *National Geographic* and also in his 2008 book, *The Blue Zones*. Now Buettner deepens his exploration into the human emotional condition in *Thrive: Finding Happiness the Blue Zones Way*, which takes a look at demographically derived "happiness hot spots" around the globe. Look for it in bookstores now ($26).

Society Updates

GeoPuzzle Answers

The Big Dip Every 12 years or so—according to the local astrological calendar—hundreds of thousands of people flock to the town of Kumbakonam, in India's Tamil Nadu state, to wash away their sins. They seek a soaking in the Mahamaham tank, a 6.2-acre step-sided pool said to contain waters from many of India's most sacred rivers. "Bathing is intimately connected with the religious life of the Hindu," noted the caption to this photo in the December 1913 *National Geographic*. "The picture shows the great tank filled with pilgrims waiting for the auspicious moment to bathe." The next Mahamaham festival is scheduled for 2016. —*Margaret G. Zackowitz*

Flashback Archive Find all the photos at **ngm.com**.

PHOTO: W. E. GRUBL, NATIONAL GEOGRAPHIC STOCK

Introduce someone special to a world of learning and fun...

NATIONAL GEOGRAPHIC KIDS is an exciting and interactive magazine for children, which makes learning fun.

Every month, readers will go on a new adventure – exploring the wonders of the natural world, getting up close with exotic wildlife, and discovering different cultures. Plus, they can test their knowledge with quizzes and puzzles, and get creative with exciting things to make and do. NATIONAL GEOGRAPHIC KIDS is everything an inquisitive young mind needs.

Let's get kids excited about their world!

Only £12 for 6 issues*

A perfect gift

More reasons to subscribe today...

- Free delivery each month
- Exclusive subscriber competitions
- NG KIDS gift card for you to send
- A saving of over 35%

THREE EASY WAYS TO SUBSCRIBE...

Fill in the coupon on the right and send to: NATIONAL GEOGRAPHIC KIDS, PO BOX 326, Sittingbourne, Kent ME9 8FA

Go to ngkids.co.uk or contact us by email at ngkids@servicehelpline.co.uk

Call our subscription hotline on 0344 322 1213†

Please quote promotion code NGK123

*Payment by Direct Debit for six issues regular price is £19.20 for six issues.

†Calls charged at 5p per minute from landline.

BEST BUY

Yes! Send **six** monthly issues of NG KIDS for only £12, paid by direct debit ☐ to me ☐ as a gift

DIRECT Debit 599674 **Instruction to your bank or building society to pay by direct debit**

To the manager [bank name] _____

Address _____

Post code _____

Name[s] of account holder[s] _____

Instructions to your bank or building society to pay direct debit
Please pay GalleonCI Ltd direct debits from the account detailed in this instruction, subject to the safeguards assured by The Direct Debit Guarantee. I understand that this instruction may remain with GalleonCI Ltd and, if so, details may be passed electronically to my bank / building society.

Branch sort code ☐☐ ☐☐ ☐☐

Bank / building society account number ☐☐☐☐☐☐☐☐

Signature[s] _____

Date _____

Yes! Send **six** monthly issues of NG KIDS for only £14, paid by credit / debit card or cheque ☐ to me ☐ as a gift

YOUR CREDIT / DEBIT CARD DETAILS
Please charge my debit card ☐ Visa Delta
Please charge my credit card ☐ Visa ☐ MasterCard ☐ American Express

Card number _____

Expiry date _____

Name as appears on card _____

Signature _____

TERMS & CONDITIONS This offer is available for subscriptions within the British Isles only (excluding BFPO addresses). All orders will be acknowledged and you will be advised of the commencement issue within 14 days. This offer cannot be used in conjunction with any other Galleonci Ltd, National Geographic or Attic Media Network Ltd subscription promotion and closes 31 May 2011. Initial six-month non-refundable contract applies. Unless written notice is given before the end of the initial term, the subscription will continue as a rolling six-month non-refundable contract. The full UK subscription rate is £38.40 for 12 issues. For subscription enquiries, please call 0844 322 1213 (if calling from outside the UK please call +44 1795 412847). By supplying your email address / mail address, you are happy to receive products and services via email / post from, or in association with, Attic Media Network Ltd / National Geographic. Please tick if you do not want to receive offers from us ☐ or third parties ☐. For our data policy, see subscribeonline.co.uk/ngkids

MY DETAILS (please fill in even if subscription is a gift)

Title _____ Surname _____

Forename _____

Address _____

Post code _____ Date of birth _____

Telephone _____

Email address _____

The subscription is a gift. Please send copies to:

Title _____ Surname _____

Forename _____

Address _____

Post code _____ Date of birth _____

Telephone _____

Email address _____

Throng Number

Puzzle by Cathy Allis

By the end of 2011 our planet will have welcomed its seven billionth inhabitant. Even the most crowded Shanghai train station (left) only hints at the vastness of the number, though this month's GeoPuzzle could give you an idea of just how big that figure really is.

ACROSS

1 Alan of *The West Wing*
5 Parks who wouldn't stand for segregation
9 Arcade game aperture
13 Penetrate slowly
14 Kind of rock or rain
15 Flight Captain Chesley Sullenberger, on January 15, 2009
16 Start of a factoid
19 Hollywood's Gardner
20 Neighbor of Minn. and Sask.
21 Laugh half
22 Factoid continued
28 Salinger title girl
29 Sch. near Monticello
30 Spoon-bending Geller
31 University of Maine's home
34 Hwy.
35 Rotisserie rod
36 Factoid continued
40 Consequently
41 Sigma preceder
42 Neighborhoods
43 Suffix with tutor
44 Freelancer's MS encl.
45 Major branch of Islam
47 Factoid continued
53 Taro-based luau dish
54 Ticonderoga, for one
55 __ de cologne
56 End of the factoid
60 Zero
61 Good at losing?
62 Don't delete
63 Mary __ Lincoln
64 Cub Scout units
65 Address for a countess

DOWN

1 Take __ at (attempt)
2 Pope after John X
3 Stick-on design
4 Letters on mil. addresses
5 Governed by chance
6 Gas-pump rating
7 Former capital of Alaska
8 Commotion
9 Comic book "Queen of the Jungle"
10 Flood barrier
11 Mined matter
12 Whole lot
17 Perfect accord
18 Spade's cousin
23 TV host Jay and his wife, Mavis
24 1984 Peace Nobelist
25 Larvae, later
26 *Baywatch* actress Eleniak
27 Confirmations and bat mitzvahs, e.g.
31 Harbor of ancient Rome
32 Where many a celeb is treated
33 Eye: prefix
34 Playmate of Piglet
35 Fine violin, for short
37 "Curses!"
38 Cry after a close call
39 Delicately pretty
44 Wasted, in a way
45 Escort from outside
46 Iroquois who share a lake's name
48 Overturn
49 Man __ hour (honoree)
50 Vaquero's lasso
51 Dog-__ (showing wear)
52 Like the floor under a sawhorse
56 Palindromic explosive
57 Go a-courting
58 Since Jan. 1, on pay stubs
59 Subj. for U.S. newcomers

Answers in Inside Geographic

How To Become A Successful Writer!

As a freelance writer, you can earn very good money in your spare time, writing the stories, articles, books, scripts etc that editors and publishers want. Millions of pounds are paid annually in fees and royalties. Earning your share can be fun, profitable and creatively fulfilling.

To help you succeed, we offer you a first-class, home study course from professional writers – individually tailored tuition – and expert personal guidance from your tutor. You learn about writing articles, stories, novels, romances, historicals, journalism, writing for children, radio, TV, the stage etc. You are advised on style, presentation, **HOW TO SELL YOUR WRITING,** copyright – and much more. In short, you learn how to be a successful writer.

If you want to be a writer, this is the way to start! It's ideal for beginners. No previous experience or special education required. You can earn while you learn. Details free – including EXPERT OPINIONS. Full refund if not successful. Visit our website or call our Freephone number now.

www.writersbureau.com

FREE CALL 24 ☎ HRS **0800 856 2008** Quote Ref: **NM1512**

✂

NAME ....
ADDRESS ....
....
.... POST CODE ....
EMAIL ....

The Writers Bureau
FREEPOST NM1512,
MANCHESTER M1 9HZ
email: 10W1@writersbureau.com
Please include your name & address

Writers Bureau **21** Years of Success

Elegance is an attitude

Kate Winslet

LONGINES®

Longines PrimaLuna

www.longines.com